T·A·K·E C·O·N·T·R·O

ALCOHOLIS
an insight into the addi

**Books supplying expert information and practical
guidance to help YOU take control**

FERTILITY
a comprehensive guide to natural family planning
Dr Elizabeth Clubb and Jane Knight

GRIEF
rebuilding your life after bereavement
Dr R. M. Youngson

OPERATION
a handbook for surgical patients
Dr Robin A. J. Youngson

RELAX AND UNWIND
a new positive approach
Jenni Adams

SCHIZOPHRENIA
a fresh approach
Gwen Howe

STROKE!
. . . a self-help manual for stroke sufferers and their relatives
Dr R. M. Youngson

Fear, fear: you speak of fear.
What is this fear? Is it the fear we dare not fear,
That fear of fear itself, or fear of other's fear,
Such fear as ends
In passionate untruth, self-justifying falsehood without end?
Daemonic fear
Of individual guilt, of being caught, of doing wrong,
And fear of failure or of being found a fool,
And fear of anything that might contrast with me
And thus reveal my insufficiency,
My lack, my weakness, my inferiority,
In showing up my difference from itself;
Fear of uncertainty and loss, fear of all change,
Fear of all strangeness and all strangers; and above all else the fear
Of Love, of being loved, of being asked for love,
Of being loved yet knowing one has no love to return;
Fear of forgiveness—
Fear of that love which is so great it can forgive

And the exhausting fear of Death and Mystery,
The Mystery of Death, of Life and Death,

 The huge appalling Mystery of everything;
 And fear of Nothing,
 Yes, after all the fear of Nothing really,
 Fear of Nothing, Nothing

Fear of Nothing, Nothing, absolutely Nothing.

      From *The Nightwatchers*, David Gascoyne

ALCOHOLISM
an insight into
the addictive mind

Dr Clive Graymore

David & Charles

A catalogue record for this book is available from the British Library

ISBN 0-7153-0026-1

Typeset by Typesetters (Birmingham) Ltd, Smethwick, West Midlands
for David & Charles
Brunel House   Newton Abbot   Devon

Printed in Great Britain by BPCC Wheatons Ltd, Exeter

Contents

To Kay, my darling wife and friend of the last twenty-five years, in gratitude for her unfailing love, understanding, and faith in my ultimate recovery, without which there would have seemed little point.

Also to Mischka, Tania, Daniel and Ellysia, our incredible children, who continually showed me both past and future, and inspired my essential hope and determination.

Also to all the staff of Broadreach House, Plymouth, England, whose dedication and compassion gave me a fresh chance of life, and to whom I am deeply grateful. And to those many others who have helped me on the way.

Foreword

A battle is not lost until the final defeat, but twenty years is a long time to be on the losing side. Yet if that proves to be the only pathway to understanding, then I believe it is justified. If that truth can be shared with others, bringing relief, or even avoiding the need for such a painful journey, then it should be seen as a privilege. I know that the greatest obstacle to my own recovery was my continuing total incomprehension of what was happening to me. Increasingly isolated from anything of value in life, I felt the ultimate isolation would be when I could stand outside myself, viewing my own life with objective and helpless horror. How could I expect others to understand, when I could not understand myself?

I was grateful in early days that occasional alcoholic lapses leading to 'uncharacteristic behaviour' were at least recognised as such by my family and friends, but as the condition progressed these lapses became sufficiently frequent and prolonged to cast doubt on the subtlety of the distinction, not only for those around me, but eventually to myself as well. I knew however that my only hope lay in some rational explanation of the apparently inexplicable, so that I could say, 'This is what happened to me; I know now what I must do'. All that, and more, is contained in this book.

A vital catalyst to recovery was given to me by Broadreach House, Plymouth, England, a treatment centre for alcoholism and other chemical dependencies. Their approach includes a highly personalised form of the acclaimed Minnesota Method developed by the Hazeldon Foundation of America. This in turn is based on many of the original precepts of Alcoholics Anonymous, whose invaluable service I heartily recommend to all recovering alcoholics. I would have done well to have been more attentive in earlier years. With considerable talent, expertise and compassion, Broadreach enabled me to see just how emotionally sick I had become, and why my guilt, pre-occupation, emotional defences and resentments precluded my remaining sober for a sufficient length of time to see the whole. Emotional chaos and dishonesty had to be stripped away, and they showed me how this could be achieved if I so chose.

Armed with sobriety and new hope, I was able to re-think my experiences. I was able to see the whole story, based on the countless people who have striven to help over many years, as well as the victims who have shared their experiences. I was able to put together events and experiences, from myself and others, both read and heard and I was able to look at the implications of the three approaches which I believe will be the mainspring of all advances that are made: Alcoholics Anonymous, NeuroElectric Therapy as developed by Dr Margaret Patterson and the Minnesota Method.

I am not even sure myself how, or when, the final piece of the puzzle fell into place, but fall it did, and the whole picture crystalised within months, each fragment of twenty years falling into place with startling simplicity. The answer was there.

Ironically, twenty years ago I had an instinctive understanding of the whole concept described in this book, but lacked the factual basis. How then could I convince anybody else and say 'I know what's happening, that's what it's all about'? I felt that whatever the problem was initially, alcohol, the 'useful remedy' only served to exacerbate it. With the passage of time my thinking became increasingly muddled, crippling my ability to cope with the real problem. I was increasingly compelled to fight the symptoms rather than the disease. Finding the evidence, and fitting theory to experience became a personal crusade.

Perhaps there is never just one approach to a problem, or one answer. But I believe the one in this book removes most of the obstacles to recovery.

Clive Graymore
Ashburton, Devon

Introduction

It would have been much simpler for me to have presented just a personal story, or to have concocted a text-book description using all the current theory and speculation, or even to have produced a step by step do-it-yourself manual. But all of these approaches would have been to some extent limiting, the first by definition, the others by nature of their coldly objective approach.

Fundamentally, addiction is an intensely human condition, and needs to be treated as such, with compassion, warmth, sincerity, even humour, but above all with honesty. Intuitively, I have always seen it in the overall context of other human ills or disturbances. It is specific only in its reference to a particular drug and its particular physical side-effects, but, generally, it reflects a lack of harmony with one's environment, a chronic 'dis-ease'. This, I think, applies equally to the causative factors as to the subsequent development. In addition, there are the underlying physiological or biochemical changes that may be explained on a molecular level.

All the information included here has been chosen with care. Some of it may seem, or be, non-applicable to certain individuals, but that is not important. It is intended as the broadest possible description of a condition, thus allowing each individual to identify sufficiently with particular aspects to make a true diagnosis, and leading them to the desire for recovery. In this sense it can be viewed as a discussion on the many aspects of the addict's world. It will enable you, whether you are victim, reader, partner, or interested party to identify with any stage, and to understand the deterioration in rational terms. This understanding is vital to the addict's recovery. Only then can the victim of addiction re-establish a firm footing on his or her particular slippery slope, pause to look upward once more, and even be aware of the pitfalls in their intended climb.

The need for adopting this general approach to a specific remedy is perhaps best illustrated and emphasised by some description of my own path. My undoubted problem and privilege in life centred on thinking too much, on never accepting but always demanding explanation. This at once explains my difficulty with religious faith and obsession with science. In the light of what I now know, it also reveals that my first skirmish with alcohol was related to my first sexual affair and my inability to resolve an attendant spiritual-intellectual conflict. I obliterated the problem and found transient delight!

Over the next few years I continued to question, and continued to drink. It would be dishonest of me not to admit that these years were good; I accrued many of the advantages of drink and experienced none of the penalties. I had a very successful career, an idyllically happy marriage and endless energy and drive. I know this pattern to be familiar in many would-be alcoholics, and I think that when we indulge in nostalgia it is right to acknowledge the good times, as well as the bad. If we forget how beautiful a dangerous woman was then we may be readily seduced again! My wife, Kay, with considerable insight, has applied the term 'Icarus Complex' to this particular phase in my life, an apt piece of terminology which I feel could be usefully incorporated into the aetiology of the disease. Many of us were victims of curiosity, would-be explorers of a tremendously exciting world, but were hampered by a complex mixture of fear and doubt, confused morality and spiritual values, or just a downright lack of equipment. How simple to fasten on our wings with wax, and like Icarus soar above convention and our self-imposed labyrinth to ever greater heights. In such a mood of confident euphoria we could not help but reach for the sun and the very Gods, but inevitably we crashed to earth. However, perhaps we should be grateful, for in some respects we experienced much and lived fully. If we choose well we will live to explore again, replacing the fallible and treacherous wax with self-knowledge and confidence.

The first hints of trouble and foreboding for the future arose some twenty years ago, when quite minor aberrations on my part rocked the apparent serenity of my existence (or was it ever really serene?) These took the form of occasional memory lapses, minor social indiscretions or unwise work decisions: nothing dramatic or important, but enough to make me question my drinking habits for the first time. In retrospect, it is now obvious that my regular alcohol intake had become perilously high, the quantity required for normal functioning having come to equate with that likely to induce intoxication. This, I believe to be the most critical and perilous time for the alcoholic. If a drink problem has not already been diagnosed, it is vital that this critical stage be recognised, for from now on we enter an entirely different ball-game.

Had I been questioned more searchingly at this time, I no doubt could have admitted to other, and potentially more serious symptoms, although I did not then recognise their true significance. I suffered from acute attacks of inexplicable apprehension, as well as a general feeling of stress and a decline in my self-confidence. My sense of purpose and direction were wavering. I was certainly more emotionally unstable. The explanation for the virtually inevitable events that were to follow is now obvious, but there was no way I could know this then, or anticipate those events. Up to this point I had allowed my alcohol intake to increase steadily, having no experience of any adverse effects that could act as a deterrent. Life could only be described as exceedingly good, and alcohol was adding fuel and zest to my living and relieving me of any debilitating doubts or fears.

As will be shown in Chapter 2, the constant and high intake of alcohol was, unbeknownst to me, destroying my natural defences against stress; and if my natural reaction to stress was poor (which was my motivation for alcohol in the first place) then I could ill afford this unwitting damage.

What was happening was that the sedative effects of the alcohol were masking my increasing hyper-sensitivity to stress. The only evidence of damage was glimpsed occasionally in times of total sobriety, which was when I experienced the unheralded acute panics. About this time I experienced, with considerable surprise, my first attack of 'shakes'. I had gone to meet the boys for the accustomed Sunday lunch-time drinks only to find myself embarrassed by being unable to lift my glass from the bar. Although I had felt uneasy before entering the bar I had attributed it to an attack of 'nerves'. In a way this was a perfectly appropriate explanation, but the fact that I had to leave the bar and down a tumbler of Scotch in one before regaining my equilibrium should have told me something. Although up to this point I had felt no overt bad effects, I had been drinking for fifteen years and, by most people's standards, very heavily in the last five – usually large neat Scotches downed in one, and for decidedly medicinal rather than social purposes.

The shakes and the panics occurred increasingly often until eventually they became a daily event, always receiving the identical therapy. The quarter-bottle in the bathroom for mornings (a glass of water first, to enable me to be sick and not waste the Scotch) the quarter-bottle in the lavatory on the train to work, the quarter-bottle everywhere for 'emergencies': cupboards, briefcases, garages, bushes, anywhere. The glass became superfluous and soon the quarter-bottle was not enough.

An interval of perhaps three or four years however separated that time of total surrender from those initial shakes in the pub and the occasional 'mishaps' that began to enter my life. I started to realise that the daily consumption of between one and two bottles of neat Scotch might be contributory to such mishaps, but it was not until I first attempted to moderate my drinking that I was compelled to recognise that I had a serious problem – for I could not do it! Like Mark Twain and smoking, I could stop, I could cut down, repeatedly. But inevitably the old pattern would re-establish itself.

It is here that the 'alcoholic plot' thickens. As we shall see in chapter 2, all that I experienced from this time can be explained in terms of chemical events over which I had no control.

Apart from, perhaps, a reckless disregard for the amount I consumed and its *potentially* injurious effects, I was guilty of no misdemeanour or crime, and was in that sense a totally innocent and unaware victim.

At the first hint of trouble I attempted in all sincerity to take the appropriate avoiding action but found myself unable to do so. As explained in chapter 2, I was devoid of either internal or external chemical defences and was unable to cope, thus hideously compounding any original problem. Original doubts had become negative certainties. And this, to a greater or lesser extent is precisely what happens to everyone who has even minimal signs of craving or addiction. As will also be shown, any drug will affect the body in precisely this same way with the same disastrous effects. Addiction is thus a self-perpetuating syndrome.

I feel physically sick when I recollect this time, and realise that all my good intentions and sincere efforts, sometimes even desperate ones, were to be of no avail, and that the end result was an abyss of self-destruction into which I would take most of what I valued. The futility of my struggles appals me. Without any understanding of the sheer chemical demand that was operating, I was powerless to ignore it. It had to be satisfied as equally as the urgent chemical demands of sleep, eating or sex. Of course I could put the cork back in the bottle, and frequently did, but at what cost, and for how long?

Having explained the 'inexplicable' in chapter 2, chapters 3–5 explain the highly predictable changes that affect the very fabric of our beings, tearing apart the values that give any meaning and purpose to our existence. From here on we are on an emotional life-support machine which permits only minimal and dwindling survival. Even should we attain sobriety, without proper understanding the diease will continue to erode our spirit, and this, as I found, leads inevitably to relapses. It was these aspects that were illuminated for me at Broadreach, and which formed a vital part of my recovery.

Alcoholism is a physical, emotional and spiritual disease. It involves the collapse of self-esteem and associated values, and the building of negative defence-systems that alienate you from society and life. A life of deep shame and chronic destructive remorse is the result, full of lies, deceit, irresponsibility, cliff-hanging survival and extravagant escape – this being the over-colourful flag of the alcoholic, the all-time loser. And all this could have been avoided: no one deliberately becomes an alcoholic.

I know now that during quite long periods of sobriety (ie, total absence of the drug) I remained both physically and emotionally sick, and this left me gravely at risk, ultimately dictating the relapses. The chemical damage as we shall see would continue to affect me both physically and emotionally for at least two years. I was incapable of any constructive repair-work as the foundations were rotten and I was totally unaware of the nature of the damage.

I attempted to contain the damage by increasing my intake of tranquilisers, which I had taken continuously for some thirty years, with or without alcohol. How was I to know that these honed in on the very sites already damaged by alcohol and could only make the situation worse? As we shall see they act synergistically: the effect of combining alcohol and tranquilisers vastly exceeds the effects of the two taken independently. When taken together they are disastrous, dangerous and unpredictable.

These factors contributed to my ultimate pattern of bout-drinking which was so destructive not only to myself but also to those around me; a period punctuated by lost jobs, financial disaster, separations, park benches, wrong beds, police cells, treatments, hospitalisations, miracle cures, 'Antabuse' implants, black-outs, convulsions, Neuro-Electric and other therapies and the Minnesota Method. Many people doubted whether I was really ill, and wondered if I was not just opting for this way of life, and many more refused to believe I wished to recover. In reality I was desperate, and I was losing, but I could not see the enemy.

Two very important points emerge. In retrospect I see that I had contracted the disease long before any of the later and more dramatic manifestations. They were just the logical progression. So do not be fooled if you do not as yet present a picture as macabre or bizarre as mine. Secondly, there can be no doubt that by any rational definition you are ill. In that sense you were not responsible for either developing the illness or for being unable to cope with the consequences. It was not your fault, and you need carry no burdensome guilt. It is vital that you should know this if you are to re-build your shattered self esteeem as explained in chapter 8.

One of the earliest casualties will be that related to the spiritual aspects of your life. We all have a spiritual side, whether we admit it or not. Put simply it is that aspect of our natures concerned with the less immediately material things, and can range from our appreciation of the smell of a rose, an erotic experience or the most obscure religion or philosophy. It concerns our feelings and values, and is perhaps more real than what we call reality; it is our ultimate sense of life, purpose and direction. There are many ways in which we sense it or interpret it, but we ignore it at our peril. Chapter 7 suggests ways you may look at this and strengthen your way forward. It is not by chance that the three most successful approaches to recovery, those of Alcoholics Anonymous, Dr Margaret Patterson and the NeuroElectric Therapy, and the Minnesota Method, emphasise the need for spiritual strength. Do not reject this aspect through arrogance.

Chapter 9 suggests that you are not unique after all, but just another example of a damaged person who happened to use alcohol or a drug to escape the hurt, and only managed to compound it in the worst possible manner. The cure proved lethal.

Until this point you had no choice, but in reading this book you will gain a complete understanding of your condition, and hence total responsibility for the future. You are being offered the choice of life.

1 Admitting the Problem

WHAT PROBLEM?

I suspect that many more people than care to admit even to themselves do have the rudiments of a problem, but it is not bad enough to justify the discomfort of abstaining. Everyone who drinks is knowingly taking a mood-altering chemical, as is the person who takes occasional tranquilisers, sleeping tablets or anti-depressants. It is a conscious desire to change one's emotional state and to that extent an admission that it is 'needed'. But much of our living consists of compromises dictated by expediency, the end hopefully justifying the means.

Imagine that alcohol had not been invented, and the tired business man (or woman) routinely took two or three tranquilisers on getting in from work ('it helps me relax'), limiting himself to a couple at lunch times of course ('otherwise my work suffers'). The tranquilisers would naturally be distributed rather more freely during parties as they helped everyone relax and lose a few inhibitions and generally promoted social and 'sexual' intercourse. I suspect that most people would find the idea of such behaviour strange, yet they act in a very similar manner, chemically speaking, with alcohol. Pretty bottles, nice glasses and a sophisticated pattern of behaviour make social drinking acceptable but most people exhibit some degree of chemical dependence.

I have no wish to see the human race robbed of one of its most delightful and, in general, harmless pleasures, but perhaps in an evolving society the *abuse* of alcohol will diminish as we recognise it for the mood-alterer it is.

The sick joke has it that the only problem alcoholics admit to experiencing is that of getting hold of the next bottle; humour, albeit bordering on the hysterical is the pathetic defence. Yet if we are honest, rare enough as we shall see, there is little mileage in *not* admitting to a problem. How else do we explain such blatantly disgusting behaviour?

In a single year I inadvertently set fire to a caravan and myself, wrote off a car and fractured three ribs, lost my licence and my job, temporarily lost my family, was admitted to hospital with a suspected coronary, bronchitis, pneumonia and pleurisy, lost six pints of blood whilst in hospital (alcoholic haemolysis) and was eventually discharged to find myself homeless. I am not proud of these achievements, and record them only to stress the absurdity of my conclusions at the end of that year: I believed the entire sequence of bizarre misadventures had stemmed from a paltry and unreasonable domestic row over a couple of drinks taken on my way home from work, causing me to seek refuge in the caravan in the first instance. I should attempt to control my reactions in the future, not allowing myself to be so readily influenced by external circumstances. What problem, indeed!

In case my horrendous inventory should exclude the reader who cannot immediately identify, I must stress that this was *not* a typical year, just one that for good reason stands out in my memory. In the somewhat less colourful preceding years I would never have accepted that this could happen to me. But it did. And although other occurrences at other times were less dramatic or less frequent, they reflected the same basic 'devaluation of self'. Whatever I may have felt at the time – and let's face it, it would have had little connection with reality – in retrospect I appreciate that an honest admission of the problem could not have tarnished my image any further!

WHAT HAVE YOU GOT TO LOSE?

If you admit that all is not well with your world, you can rest assured that such a confession will meet with enthusiastic common agreement, but unfortunately it is unlikely to evoke much sympathy. For not only is alcoholism probably the most overall destructive disease known to man, but it is also unique in being the only disease in which the victim is held responsible for his complaint, his symptoms and the consequences. He is censured morally, and punished legally or through a variety of social and domestic sanctions. For most people alcohol is associated with the pursuit of pleasure, and in most societies the excessively self-indulgent pursuit of pleasure is regarded as a sin, and as such deserving of punishment. Every red-blooded male loves a pretty girl, but acceptance of that does not condone unconditional seduction. I am explaining this not in a mood of retrospective self-pity, but in an attempt to establish the terrible reality of the situation, the understanding of which is vital both to the alcoholic and those who care. The anguish of the alcoholic is made all the more nightmarish by his recognition that his protests will be misinterpreted as self-pity, or seen as no more than 'just deserts'. I found it essential to try to understand both attitudes in assessing my own position.

In some respects I was fortunate in that my wife is a committed diarist, recording most events and sometimes attendant emotional impact. The role of alcohol in family life was only incidental to her writings, but they allowed me, sometimes most painfully to participate in some of her feelings over many years, to see myself as she saw me and to reflect on situations as she interpreted them. It is apparent that in the later stages some of the more dramatic incidents were misread by either or both parties and that alcohol was effectively obliterating real communication. It is certainly a tribute to the quality of her love and her faith that her few escapes were transient and more than justified. This observation is not a personal irrelevancy. As the alcoholic comes to understand the real nature of his or her disease there is a considerable danger of over-compensation, of adopting a self-righteous approach to events of the past. 'I was sick, what was your excuse, how could you treat me like that!' You might recollect that even you could not understand yourself at the time, so why demand such objective expertise from your partner? You have to accept that your behaviour was probably abominable and often extremely hurtful, especially to those closest to you, and far worse than you are likely to recollect. It is also presumptuous to assume that the behaviour of someone close to you would remain impeccable when they were forced, or chose, to live in the sphere of your alcoholic influence. The induced emotional disturbance of the partner has long been recognised in practice and there is evidence that a similar stress syndrome is produced biochemically in the partner (possibly the cortical insufficiency syndrome, see Greer). Tragically, the closer the relationship the more disastrous the effect.

Whatever the misinterpretations involved, the alcoholic suffers from a hideous disease inflicting untold harm on those around them. Is it really preferable for both you and others to assume this is the 'normal' you? Or better to admit that you have a problem? Admitting to the problem will bring relief and new hope to all concerned, and there will be no shortage of help or sympathy when the true nature of the condition is explained and concrete action is taken to remedy it.

If the lunatic doubts his sanity, it is said that he is well on the way to recovery. This 'catch 22' situation is only too familiar to the drinker and carries two implicit problems. How ill, and what is he going to do about it?

IT IS EVEN WORSE THAN IT SEEMS

At the height, or depths, of his illness the drinker will almost certainly be incapable of recognising just how bizarre his life has become. God may have deserted his particular heaven, and all is definitely not well with his world, but he is so frantically preoccupied with clearing up the mess that he has little time to appreciate the true extent of the damage. In fact, as we shall see, his main concern is remedying the symptoms rather than the disease itself, the symptoms being the endless real and imaginary disasters that confront him. Coping and surviving are the immediate aims of a very immediate life, and he is unable to comprehend that in the long term neither of these objectives is even remotely attainable.

The unfortunate example I have cited from my past is a case in point. Even during that ill-fated year I would not admit that I was ill. My illness was such that I was incapable of judging the whole, attempting only to rationalise and explain each isolated event in the sequence. So what chance in less desperate yet often equally unreal times? For many years, in my particular case, the only problems clouding my otherwise blue skies were relatively minor worries concerning finance, or small moral indiscretions. Yet I was treading the same path even then, but the scenery was imperceptibly changing. I chose to ignore the signposts carefully planted by those who had gone before, and in any event, without the eventual understanding, could not have turned back. It takes considerable courage to look at one's life and recognise it as the disaster it has become.

The second problem is that if one does recognise that one is sick, then one is under an obligation to do something about it. The only remedy is to forego liquor, an approach heartily endorsed by all concerned. Simplicity itself. Yet thousands die every year rather than adopt this simple remedy. To be optimistic about such a simple prescription is akin to telling someone they can avoid the spots providing they do not catch the measles. It seems logical that removing 'drink' from a 'drink problem' may well leave a 'problem'.

On those occasions when I would actually pause to wonder about the true nature of my predicament, I would invariably be defeated by the variety of the symptomology. I would not deny that the ingestion of alcohol played a not inconsiderable part in the aetiology, but exactly how eluded me. And why me? Like many, I had long cherished the hope that I had some mission in life, but hopefully it was not as a walking aversion therapy for others tempted by the demon drink! Nevertheless, for some reason I was unwilling to accept that my plight had any organic basis, a reluctance I have found to be not uncommon in alcoholics. Perhaps it is because we are also affected by the very prejudices about over-indulgence in pleasure that cause society to condemn us, and cannot readily dissociate the intense misery of our present state from happier days of drinking in the past. The ephemeral guilt of a riotous night in our youth grows deeply entrenched. It becomes a permanent, destructive and drink-demanding guilt.

I had to attribute my sense of failure to some weakness, not of body, but of mind or spirit. In spite of being a neurochemist, I chose to ignore the obvious fact that even psychical phenomena often operated at a molecular level. I was almost being masochistic, punishing myself by accepting full blame and responsibility.

PERSONALITY TRAIT?

Because I knew alcoholism to be recognised as a 'familial' disease, occurring with increased frequency in certain family lines, I had felt instinctively for many years that it was probably a secondary mani-festation of some other inherited factor that predisposed the individual to using alcohol. As far as I could envisage, the most obvious predisposing factor had to evidence itself as a personality trait. Like many who had repeatedly sought help, I had 'enjoyed' more than my fair share of psychoanalysis, unfortunately without any beneficial results.

I had experienced some unremarkable disturbances before the development of a drink problem, and sporadically I would attempt to relate these to the present and overwhelming disaster. Around the age of twelve, my incredibly happy childhood had been inter-rupted by a year of compulsive behaviour rooted in either shame or guilt, no doubt sexually inspired, and some ten years later I fell victim to a variety of bizarre psychosomatic symptoms associated with the combined emotional stress of crucial examinations and my first affair. These interludes raised questions about my ability to cope with stress. In my early drink years they would be seized on by enthusiastic psychiatrists and the entire package attributed to a traditional traumatic happening at the age of two when I was separated from my parents by meningitis. The fact that I screamed my head off for three weeks whilst in isolation substantiated their views that I had received considerable trauma, and a resulting sense of insecurity. Every child in the isolation ward however did *not* scream his head off, fortunately for the caring staff, so why me? The same question. Why me?

It suddenly seemed obvious that *circumstances* had not contrived to make me insecure, I *was* insecure! I had yelled because I could not cope readily, any more than I could at twelve, or in my twenties, or now. The first event did not cause the following, they were all symptoms of a common cause, an inborn personality trait.

So perhaps the would-be alcoholic's impaired ability to cope with stress caused his need to use drink. These self-searchings revealed little that was new to me, for I had already been classified as an 'anxiety bout-drinker' a concept that was very fashionable at the time, and on which I seized to divorce myself from the more damaging label of 'alcoholic'. However it did little to allay either the criticism or fears of those around me, and even less to help me:

OK, so you worry too much, that makes you drink, that makes you ill, not to mention irresponsible and bloody-minded. So stop drinking, and stop worrying.

Since I was as incapable of avoiding stress as I was of avoiding the next bottle, this was no answer, although it helped convince me that my own theory was not without foundation. I appeared to be stuck with both these chronic manifestations of a personality aberration. I saw myself, and others like me, as a slightly emotionally damaged person who had sought refuge in drink, but who, as a result of the cure had become grossly sick, both increasingly unable to cope with stress without drink, and unable to cope with the cure. I had long since ceased to be able to distinguish the emotional chaos that led to further drinking from that which resulted from it.

Although I was beginning to establish some semblance of a pattern for my behaviour, making it marginally more acceptable to myself, if not those around me, there seemed no way I could progress from such an unconstructive conclusion. I was still held fast by the frightening vicious circle catch-22 situation. Prolonged sobriety was essential if I wished to understand truly either myself or the problem, but the actual problem was that of maintaining sobriety. However, had I but known it, I was remarkably close to the truth as I see it today.

THE COMMITMENT

I had known for some time that sobriety certainly did not bring serenity. Eventually only the Broadreach Clinic could explain the reason for this and provide the necessary help. But to start with this remarkable treatment centre does not *tell* you anything. With expertise, dedication and compassion, their skilled psychotherapy draws the answers from within you, so that you become author of your own destiny.

They also teach you that initially, in seeking help, only you can find your real motivation. You have to realise firstly (as with Alcoholics Anonymous) that you are powerless over alcohol and secondly that your life is in considerable chaos as a result of this. Obviously the severity of the problem will vary considerably, and each individual must assess his or her own situation honestly, but there is no doubt that this is a vital first stage; explanations can follow. My deliberations and rationalisations had got me nowhere for no amount of explanation will prevent a return to drink unless that motivation has been established.

You *need* to stop drinking, but you need to know *why* you do. The essential first stage, therefore, is to decide for yourself whether you have a real problem of addiction, or not. By addiction, we mean some dependence on a mood-altering chemical which you feel powerless to control, and which is making your life unmanageable, or is likely to. If the condition is advanced, it is irrelevant to ask whether life is better or worse with the substance. What you must do is ask whether this is how you wish to live, and whether you can continue to live in this way, and live with yourself, bearing in mind that your life *will* undoubtedly get worse?

It is vital to ask this basic question. Only then do you have the choice to shake off the self-made but illusory cage which is in a nightmarish way closing in on you, restricting both your vision and your behaviour in an ever-tightening grip. The illusion can be shattered by understanding, the 'cage' vanish, light replace dark. You can be free to 'take up your bed and walk'. This you need to know. If you take responsibility for your problem it will be revealed as a disease for which you were not to blame, for you had no way of recognising the damage you were causing yourself and how this damage subverted your entire personality creating the helplessness of your present state.

WHAT IS ALCOHOLISM?

Much apprehension surrounds the word 'alcoholic', for it implies inadequacy, an unseemly past, and an uncertain, even sterile, future. It is seen as not just a name, but a way of life, or death. It is difficult for someone whose whole life has been characterised by excess to ask suddenly to be seen as 'tamed'. But the Christians in the lions' den would have been delighted, and so will every right-thinking friend or associate of yours.

It is obvious that there is a very wide and varied spectrum of problems related to alcohol, and drugs. Until such time therefore as some distinction is made between the different forms of the problem there is little benefit to be obtained in using one name rather than another: alcoholic, alcoholism, problem drinker, habitual drunk, continual over-imbiber, drug addict . . . I believe they will all respond to the treatment offered here, and that is all that should concern us.

I do not myself particularly appreciate the term 'alcoholic', preferring to see myself as suffering from 'alcoholism', a condition stemming from my unwitting overuse of alcohol. The distinction is small but it fits more comfortably. If it is eventually established that the condition results directly from a genetic and metabolic flaw then the distinction will vanish.

The popular media tend to promote only the extreme images of alcoholism and addiction. It is hardly surprising that few of us can readily identify with these exaggerated images. The uncertain and curious who attend their first meetings of Alcoholics Anonymous frequently slip through the net, failing to relate to those they meet. This is unfortunate, for though they may be at a very early stage of the disease, it is probably a crucial one.

AA, whom I regard most highly, do tend to perpetuate two myths which can sometimes have unfortunate results: that only the alcoholic knows that he is an alcoholic and no-one can tell him, and that he has to reach his personal rock bottom before recovery. Admittedly there is considerable practical evidence to support the unhappy truth of these statements, but it might be more compassionate to be able to tell someone they were an alcoholic, preferably *before* they had lost most of what they value in life. Considering the disastrous emotional effects of the disease it seems ironic that we should rely on self-diagnosis by someone with a malfunctioning sense of judgement. Improved prognosis by early diagnosis is assumed in other diseases, so why is alcoholism seen as the exception? I hope that the information in this book will lead to diagnosis at an early stage.

So the newcomer to AA or the treatment centre may well be caught in the familiar and notorious 'that has not happened to me' syndrome, failing to hear or accept the chorus of 'not yet'. Yet the sick person should not need to prove his illness by losing his job, family, home, driving licence, liberty or sanity. It is all surprisingly predictable, but it took me over a decade for my personal 'not yet' to become 'now'. When it did, it bore a very close resemblance to all I had refused to accept could happen to me.

So the alcoholic may genuinely fail to diagnose his problem, or be reluctant to do so. (If for no other reason, the terms 'alcoholic' or 'alcoholism' are useful and significant as they do imply a commitment to sobriety essential to recovery). That being so, he is offered the alternative of being a Problem Drinker, for this he cannot dispute. If he assumes there to be a difference, and personally I believe it to be largely a matter of degree (apart from obvious exceptions), then he believes he does not necessarily have to opt for total abstinence. This may enable him to hang on for another few years and prove he was wrong. I did!

By 'obvious exceptions' I am referring to those who become drunk and irresponsible with unreasonable frequency, thus causing problems, without any signs of a permanent dependence. The genuine 'take it or leave it' types who just prefer to take it. They may well opt for a controlled-drinking approach. Space prevents me commenting on the evidence for and against this method. Suffice it to say that I believe those who have a serious problem, as can be determined by the end section of this chapter, should not be tempted. I have yet to meet the confessed alcoholic who has not tried controlled drinking and failed, and others are dead as a result. Without knowing individual circumstances I cannot say it will not work. But imagine placing a hundred bullets in a basket of which perhaps four or five are duds, selecting one at random and firing it at your head. That is the type of gamble you are planning. You too can be a guinea pig, albeit a dead one.

Most people arriving at AA meetings or admitting themselves to treatment centres are pretty desperate people, usually with good reason. Not infrequently they are stoned out of their minds and ready to admit all, sign anything, providing the nightmare is removed. There is initially a sense of relief; the problem has been handed over. Unfortunately this feeling is often transient, a partial return to 'normality' causing them to question the wisdom of their decision. 'What's a nice guy/girl like me doing in a joint like this' and similar variations punctuate their thoughts, frequently loudly expressed over the next few hours. It would be funny if it were not so sad and familiar. This demonstrates most clearly the amazing ability of the mind to minimise the pain of the immediate past, let alone the more distant past.

So how do we go about assessing our addictive or alcoholic status? The answer is simple. Methodically, painstakingly, logically. It has probably taken us a few years to reach the stage where we are forced to question ourselves, and it is potentially capable of taking, and wasting, even more years. Is it not reasonable then to spend some hours answering ourselves? Even a few days?

The most important qualifications are honesty and courage. Courage is undoubtedly necessary, for if you are truly honest the process will be painful. The pain is a telling indication and will help to further your conviction. The answers must be as objective as possible. In the past both causes and effects were justified by excuses and rationalisations. We had to do this in order to live with ourselves and with drink or drugs. But there is no place for them now. How can all this be achieved?

POWERLESSNESS

The idea of being powerless is closely associated with the whole concept of addiction and chemical dependence. We can, of course, be dependent on many things in life and frequently feel varying degrees of need. It is the urgency of this psychological and physical need that constitutes addiction and our inability to ignore this need.

Throughout every stage the alcoholic not only needs the alcohol, but *thinks* he needs it. The vital role of psychological dependence is not always fully recognised and is probably the most powerful reason for that first drink. 'I know the pain will go if I have a drink'. Most addicts of any kind will be familiar with the relief of the first shot. Panic is removed within seconds, in anticipation of the physiological effect. The relief is psychological: a calming effect can be obtained by the mere presence of a bottle, or panic induced by its absence. The alcoholic comes to assume that things can only improve again if he accepts that drink. This conditioning is very powerful, explaining why the alcoholic who has abstained for a period starts drinking again. It might be argued that the horrific consequences that invariably follow must act as a form of aversion therapy. But the instant reward system operates here, and this is all that matters, and the alcoholic still assumes that on this occasion he will not carry the exercise to its extreme. When he feels better he will be able to think . . .! All this emphasises the importance of recognising psychological dependence, which together with the chemical addiction, leads to our powerlessness.

THE PROJECT

To carry out this essential project I suggest you use a notebook, preferably loose-leaved, using one side only and writing on every other line. This will allow adequate space for ongoing alterations or additions. Remember, be as accurate as possible, for only total honesty will bring any rewards. Any hope of recovery depends on this. Do not exaggerate, or unnecessarily colour the account. If you are an alcoholic it will have quite sufficient colour without addition. On the other hand, and more important, do not *minimise*. Alcoholism has not been termed the 'Disease of Denial' for nothing. Whilst drinking we habitually deny how much we drink and the extent of the effects, both to others and ourselves. Construct a table, chart, or an accurate account of the amount, type and frequency of drinking from the very first drink, year by year as far as honest recollection allows. Look for trends, changes in frequency, amount and type of liquor consumed. Note when you did not drink, be it days or weeks. Note also any remembered 'black' areas of extreme drinking. Finally, just to depress yourself – for a good cause – estimate the cost involved. (In most cases, this will be small relative to the hidden costs.)

When appraising your results, remember two common misconceptions. Firstly, although quantity is often equated with alcoholism, it is not the hallmark. Frequency may be a better indicator of dependence. Secondly, one of the most constant features of alcoholism is unpredictability. The popular view of the alcoholic is the 'one sherry trifle and he's finished' variety. Not so. Such cases of *immediate* and uncontrolled disaster are rare, for the victim would be remarkably short lived.

Having done this you should have some picture of your drinking habits, and then you can determine whether your condition has noticeably worsened. But before you draw any conclusions you must first come to terms with the *effects*. Again, be methodical, and try to remember dates, times and places. Avoid random and inaccurate recollections. It should be as comprehensive as possible, suggested headings including: family, social, work, finance, physical, spiritual, emotional, behavioural, legal, sexual and moral. Somewhere in these categories room should be found for all bizarre happenings such as black-outs, memory losses, hallucinations, fits, lying, deceit, hiding, accidents, physical damage to oneself or others, cheating, forging, stealing, conning, verbal or physical abuse, suicide impulses and changes affecting your morality, integrity, value systems, honesty or general well-being. Think really clearly, for if you work methodically and honestly through the list you will be astounded by the manner in which your life has been affected. Yes, concealing a bottle is deceitful, minimising the amount drunk or the money spent is lying, using the housekeeping money to include a bottle of wine is cheating, and you might not have leapt into bed with Fred or Flossie without that drink. It may well depress you and so it should, but look on it as the nasty medicine essential to recovery. Even more important, remember *this is not you*. It is the effect of the alcohol on you. Then consider what alcohol has done to your self-respect and try writing a few notes on this.

Have you considered there may be areas in which you are finding difficulty in coping? These could be pressures within the family, stresses at work, finance, or even something as simple as the daily shopping, housework, household bills or maintenance, social events, or it might be some moral or spiritual tussle. Try to think through your life at this moment and ask yourself whether you are really coping with life as you would wish, or have some areas become unmanageable? Alcohol makes immediate demands on health, money, time and energy, and causes a deterioration in behaviour as well as general powers of concentration, commitment and concern. A preoccupation with drink will eventually exclude all other priorities, all other values. Look to see where these and other alcohol-linked problems are reducing your ability to manage your affairs as efficiently as you would wish. Remember that the first and essential step for recovery in Alcoholics Anonymous requires an admission that you have become powerless over alcohol and that as a result your life has become unmanageable.

CONTROL

Now have an equally honest look at your attempts to control drinking. State the method (free will, AA, hospitalisation, therapy and so on) and the period of success. It should not be difficult to prove that if you have tried previously, such efforts were doomed to failure, otherwise it is unlikely you would be reading this book. Alcoholics often are characterised by their inability to predict where that first drink will lead them. They may not drink for lengthy periods. They may manage to control their drinking, usually for less lengthy periods. They even manage to simulate social drinking for a while. But sooner or later, without apparent cause or pre-meditation, they prove their powerlessness. This is well marked in the bout drinker. Had they but known it, any one of those drinks during the apparent quiet period could have triggered the next catastrophe. They could not predict. Ask yourself honestly whether you knew when the last excess was about to start?

If you have carried out your task effectively, I am quite prepared to let you wallow in guilt and shame – at the moment. It is very important that you should re-experience all that you have written. For a full and meaningful recovery you will have to learn to feel again and to express your feelings with honesty. The average alcoholic will protest at this point, 'But that's my problem. I feel too much'. Nonsense. I mean basic, strong, honest feelings.

2 The Disease Concept

The validity of ascribing disease status to alcoholism is frequently questioned by moralists. Legal, social and moral irresponsibility accompanying over-indulgence in intoxicating liquor is unlikely to inspire either sympathy or compassion. The answer, 'Stop drinking', seems so simple to the outsider, yet is so impossible for the victim. This startling discrepancy can only be explained by some disease concept which directly concerns the judgement, will and behaviour of the alcoholic. That *is* the disease of alcoholism, the so-called remedy only underlining the problem.

'You are not sick, you just enjoy drinking' is occasionally understandable as a rebuke stemming from frustration, but engenders justifiable bitterness in the helpless recipient. He knows he is sick, but who will listen?

The alcoholic desperately wishes to rejoin the human race, but is unable to relinquish alcohol. His attempts to satisfy both these needs leads to an elaborate web of deceit and manoeuvering which is construed as selfish attempts to have the best of both worlds.

All this was appreciated as early as 1935 by the American Medical Association who generously conceded that alcoholics were 'valid patients', and in 1952 by the World Health Organisation who noted 'interference with mental and bodily health' requiring treatment. More significantly, in 1956, the AMA defined alcoholism as a slow, progressive and incurable disease and forced legislation requiring hospitals to accept alcoholics for treatment. However, the fact that 95 per cent of alcoholics choose to ignore specialist advice and die is bound to inspire cynicism, and reluctance to accept alcoholism as a distinct clinical entity persists (Heather and Roberston 1985).

Half a century ago, three 'end of the liners' founded the first Alcoholics Anonymous group in Akron, Ohio. They opened the eyes and minds of the world to alcoholism and offered the first real and practical help to thousands of sufferers. It was not until after World War II that many of their principles and concepts were incorporated into sophisticated modern treatment techniques forming the basis of what we now know as the Minnesota Method, (after the State in which it originated). From its very inception A.A. has insisted that alcoholism is a disease affecting people physically, emotionally and spiritually, and that all these areas have to be considered together in recovery. The Minnesota Method employs skilled pscyhotherapy to locate the damage and rectify it.

Not surprisingly two areas have come under attack from the more cynically disposed; the disease concept and the spiritual implications. Much of the criticism results from misunderstanding or plain semantics.

ALL IN THE FAMILY

Alcoholism is known to occur with unexpectedly high frequency in certain families, and this observation has led to the suggestion that the condition might be inherited, transmitted through our genes. Many characteristics are dictated by the information passed on by our genes at conception, including on occasion abnormal characteristics causing disease. Inheritance of alcoholism would endorse an organic disease basis, and this is often used to support the idea.

Life would be very dull if we were stamped out in set moulds, however, and nature includes many devices ensuring 'variety in conformity'. Even for a given set of genes, for example, our environment may well also influence the outcome, and arguments continue to rage over the relative roles of gene and environment. A healthy tan, for example, requires the appropriate gene for pigmentation *and* exposure to sun; and controversy still surrounds the relative roles of gene and social environment on intelligence, or even in certain behavioural traits. These are spoken of either as

A-C

inherited or acquired characteristics. A further possibility in determining our fates concerns the inheritance of a predisposition, or enhanced susceptibility, to some agent or environmental factor. A weak stomach or cardiovascular system may be inherited but not manifest itself unless subjected to trauma, such as stress, smoking or alcohol.

If alcoholism were the result of a faulty gene which resulted in say, an abnormal pathway of alcohol breakdown leading invariably to addiction, then the recurrence of the disease in a particular family tree should obey the laws of heredity and follow an established genetic pattern. Such a mechanism has been postulated and will be described, but the expected genetic pattern is not apparent. On the other hand, if only a pre-disposition is inherited, the development of the disease would depend on two variables, the extent of the predisposition and the degree of contact with the environmental agent, which we can assume in this case to be alcohol. The presence of these two variables would produce a less distinct pattern, although circumstances and social pressures would contrive to produce a greater incidence of alcolholism than could be accounted for by chance in a particular family line. Diseases showing this pattern are described as familial, rather than genetic. I believe alcoholism to be a familial disease, the inherited pre-disposition evidencing itself as a personality trait.

Reports on the influence of heredity vary. According to Patterson, Dr David Smith of the Haight-Ashbury Free Medical Clinic in San Francisco, California, claims that the child of an alcoholic parent is 35 times more likely to become addicted than one of non-alcoholic parents. Where both parents are alcoholic this factor is increased to 400. The potentially disastrous effects of home environment cannot be disregarded in such cases, but Goodwin states that the incidence is increased fourfold even when the child of an alcoholic is adopted in infancy; significantly this figure was matched by their siblings who remained at home with the natural parents, thus casting doubt on the role of environment in these instances.

The classical approach to any genetic study is that based on identical and non-identical twins, in which it can be assumed that only the former have an identical genetic make-up, and provides an ideal technique for distinguishing between genetic or environmental factors. Heather and Robertson report a Scandinavian study in which a 70 per cent concordance rate for chronic alcoholism was shown in identical twins. A similarity of drinking patterns was observed in non-identical twins but on a less dramatic scale. But other studies have failed to produce such striking results. Many studies are bedevilled by a lack of good statistical treatments eradicating all variables and it seems likely that both genetic and environmental factors play a part. Children react to a background of alcoholism in a 'passive-aggressive' manner, having difficulty in expressing assertive impulses, and imitation or stress may well be involved.

The tendency is to assume that behavioural disorders transmitted from one generation to another are some reaction to adverse circumstances. Insufficient attention is paid to the possibility that some aspects of behaviour may reflect some abnormal pattern of body chemistry which is genetically transmitted. There is increasing evidence to suggest that minute changes in certain biochemicals may well play a hitherto unsuspected role in abnormal behaviour patterns which were more commonly ascribed to upbringing and environment. This supports my concept of an inherited personality trait in alcoholism.

The importance of any genetic connection in the disease concept justifies some comment on animal studies. Certain strains of rat show a greater preference for very dilute alcohol solutions than normal controls who wisely prefer pure water, indicative of a genetic motivation. Even more striking, this preference can be increased by cross breeding the 'heavy drinkers'. This suggests that in rats there is undoubtedly a genetic mechanism operative in their preference for alcohol. Separate experiments have shown that conditions of stress will cause normal rats to shift their preference to alcohol, suggesting that a change in emotional status may be involved, and be the primary genetic factor.

MATTER OVER MIND

The power of mind over matter is recognised, but neurophysiology has also taught us the applications of the reverse. This theme was taken up by sociobiology in works such as *The Genetic Evolution of Social Behaviour* by W. D. Hamilton and *On Human Nature* by E. Wilson who saw the mind as an epiphenomenon of the brain, stressing the physical basis of mind. Richard Dawkins' celebrated work *The Selfish Gene* appeared in 1978 and hinted at the possibility that we were little more than elaborate survival devices for transmitting the all-powerful gene.

The functioning of a car is dependent on, and limited by the sum total of its moving parts, but much of its behaviour depends on the driver. It seems reasonable to accept that the gene dictates the basic design of our molecular architecture, and this in turn describes the mental and physical parameters available to us. The moral dilemma involves our usage of the 'space' provided. There is a natural reluctance to accept that our social behaviour, even our basic emotional states, may be governed at least in part, by the chemistry of our brains. It seems to take away our sense of personal responsibility or free will, all credit for the good we do, all blame for the evil. Yet we accept limitations imposed on us genetically in a physical sense, and tend to order our lives accordingly. We, of all people, are only too aware of the role of mood-altering chemicals in reorganising our brain chemistry, and thereby inducing sleep or euphoria, reducing tension, pain or depression.

Some of the most exciting advances in our understanding of behaviour have emerged recently in research into neuro-transmitters, a fairly large group of substances responsible, amongst other things, for the subtle differential interplay of nerve transmissions in the brain. Certain of these (norepinephrine, dopamine and serotonin) are thought to be concerned with emotional states, and high levels contribute to euphoria, low levels to pain or depression. High levels are associated with exciting and fun-loving personalities with a marked ability to get into trouble. The actual levels seem to be controlled by the monamine oxidases, enzymes which break them down; high oxidase activity will lower their levels leading to depression. If we inhibit the oxidases this depression should be lifted, hence the use of such inhibitors in the successful treatment of certain forms of depression, and their implication in a variety of behavioural disorders.

Whilst we remain uncertain as to exactly what we mean by such ill-defined feelings as fear, stress, anger or euphoria, it is obviously over-optimistic to hope to link them with precise chemical configurations. Nevertheless it is becoming apparent that such feelings are under chemical control.

Dr. Badway, writing in the *British Journal on Alcohol and Alcoholism* reminds us that not only pain, but fear and anxiety are under neurochemical control.

MIND OVER MATTER

It would be foolish to blind ourselves to the endogenous chemical control of behaviour, or to deny that genetically we may be implanted with our own highly personalised survival kit at birth, which may be adequate or not according to our needs. It would be equally foolish not to accept that within certain limits, we may be subject to emotional constraints with which we must live, not dissimilar to those that govern our other mental and physical attributes. But this does not deny that which we know as free-will or choice. There is adequate manoeuvering space within the limits, and our task is to use this potential fully. Our interreaction with our environment plays a vital role in modification or adaptation. The effects of psychotherapy and social reforms, or lack of them, underline the ability to modify or change. Experience continually provides us with this possibility of change, and therefore with choice. The cybernetics are complex, the causal relationships obscure, but if we accept the role of matter over mind, we must turn full circle and remind ourselves of the enormous powers of mind over matter.

We cannot disregard the chemical reality of an inherited personality which might rightly constitute the genetic factor in alcoholism, possibly enhancing our susceptibility to alcohol indirectly through an adverse reaction to stress.

THE ANATOMY OF A DISEASE

Dr. David Owen, a leading authority on alcoholism in the States points out that more is known about alcoholism than about cancer or diabetes, yet we do not question the validity of calling these diseases. The disease fits into a classical picture with known symptoms that can be readily diagnosed, and a known pathogenesis (course) and prognosis; out of every 36 patients, 35 will die as a result of alcohol, and 0.5 (statistically) will go insane. Those that do escape skid row usually do so by courtesy of some traumatic incident. Doubts regarding aetiology (cause) or therapy are no more than those surrounding other major killers.

A variety of minor or major disturbances have been detected in alcoholism but it has not been possible to separate cause from effect, most probably resulting from excessive alcohol intake.

A BIOCHEMICAL DISEASE? THE TIQ MODEL

Perhaps the most important advance noted in the last decade is that emanating from an initial observation in Houston, Texas. Fresh brain tissue was urgently required for cancer research, and the local 'winos', skid row alcoholics, unwittingly provided a supply of this material after death. During the course of the research investigators were surprised to conclude – falsely as it transpired – that these end-of-the-liners were also addicted to heroin. They were not, of course, barely affording the cheapest liquor, but what they had found in the brains of all these alcoholics was a substance closely related to heroin, tetrahydroisoquinoline, or TIQ. This substance had been used briefly as a pain killer in World War II, but rapidly withdrawn due to its highly addictive nature. The significance of this accidental finding was immediately recognised and further research followed.

As noted already, most strains of rat in the absence of stress, when offered a choice between water and very dilute alcohol will opt for the former. Rats specially selected for their positive dislike of alcohol were treated with TIQ, and without the introduction of any external trauma the rats immediately acquired an alcoholic disposition, choosing to ignore the pure water. Professor Robert Myers of the University of North Carolina's Centre for Alcohol Studies extended these opiate studies to macaque monkeys, providing a more appropriate bio-chemical analogue, and obtained similar results. He predicted the development of appropriate drugs that would halt the addiction of the alcoholic, finding, for example, that anti-opiate drugs such as naloxone reduced the preference of the treated rats. Interestingly, it was found that TIQ remained in the brains of monkeys for considerable periods, even years. It was suggested that this might explain the rapid deterioration of alcoholics who resume drinking after many years of sobriety. It has not, to my knowledge, been ascertained whether this applies to endogenously produced natural TIQs.

TIQs are chemically very similar to naturally occurring opiates produced in the brain and known as enkephalins or endomorphins (endorphins). These substances, as we shall see, form an elaborate defence-system against mental or physical trauma, conversely, contributing to pleasure. Although there is not universal agreement on the highly addictive effects of TIQs, there seems little doubt that they enhance the pleasure obtained from drinking, and hence contribute to addiction.

In the normal individual alcohol is broken down by the liver to form, in the first instance, acetaldehyde. This substance is then broken down via a series of reactions into carbon dioxide and water, which are then eliminated from the body. Dr Peters of the Clinical Research Centre, Harrow, Middlesex, has discovered that many alcoholics have a much lower level of an enzyme responsible for the second stage, the conversion of acetaldehyde to acetic acid. This will cause an accumulation of acetaldehyde which, it is thought, reacts with certain neurotransmitters in the brain, such as dopamine, to form the opiate TIQs which are perhaps responsible for the addiction. Significantly he has shown that the level of this crucial enzyme remains depressed even after prolonged 'drying out'.

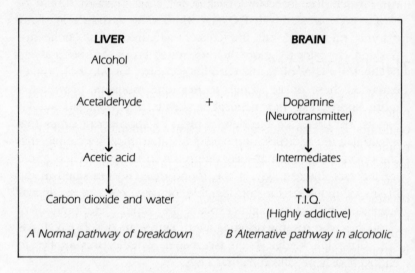

LIVER		BRAIN
Alcohol		
↓		
Acetaldehyde	+	Dopamine (Neurotransmitter)
↓		↓
Acetic acid		Intermediates
↓		↓
Carbon dioxide and water		T.I.Q. (Highly addictive)
A Normal pathway of breakdown		B Alternative pathway in alcoholic

This appears to happen only in the brains of alcoholics, not 'normal' drinkers, thus for the first time suggesting an abnormal metabolic pathway leading to pronounced addiction. There are many neurotransmitters and it is now known they can all react with acetaldehyde producing variant TIQs.

On the surface, a perfectly simple explanation of alcoholism: a genetic flaw leading to an enzyme deficiency which in turn stimulates production of a highly addictive opiate which causes alcoholism. But until such time as evidence for the deficiency *preceding* ingestion of alcohol is obtained, the possibility cannot be ruled out that these observable effects *result* from alcohol abuse, rather than causing it.

A picture should nevertheless be emerging gradually to suggest that the alcoholic may be a victim of some type of metabolic disorder, some abnormality of body chemistry, and that there may be a significant genetic factor involved. In this sense he cannot be held responsible for the development of the disease, or its catastrophic consequences. This, however, does not absolve him from the responsibility for controlling his problem in the future, once he understands how this can be achieved. Before we draw any further conclusion, let us look back over a typical pattern.

THE EVIDENCE

Alcohol probably affected you in a different way from the way it did others from that very first drink, but you were not to know this and could not appreciate the significance. Early drinking days could be typified by the apparent *absence* of a problem, with light payment for the marked beneficial effects. A typical picture in the early stages shows an individual who has a high tolerance of alcohol, rarely becomes drunk or incapable, and rarely suffers the after effects exhibited by others. The traditional hangover seems not to occur. This person is the envy rather than the butt of his fellows. Yet there is strong evidence, based on subjective analyses, to suggest that both quantitatively and qualitatively the beneficial effects for this person are enhanced. In the would-be alcoholic, the lift is not only greater but more enduring. There are also other patterns that mark out some potential alcoholics, ranging from active dislike of the taste of liquor to an almost obsessional preoccupation with the whole aura of drinking. Interpretation of these phenomena must be left to psychiatry.

Between these early stages, a kind of honeymoon phase, and the later highly destructive stages of the disease, a more sinister pattern gradually emerges. The duration of each period will vary with the individual, depending on physiological and mental make-up. The general trend can best be shown by a simple diagram contrasting the typical patterns of the alcoholic and the normal drinker (see Figure 1). The straight line depicts the personality between pain on the one hand and euphoria on the other. The diagram supposes an average well-adjusted personality which balances between the two extremes, experiencing no more than its fair share of pain and pleasure (an ideal but unlikely situation for most of us). In the normal individual the anaesthetising affects of alcohol shift the balance temporarily towards the more pleasurable end of the spectrum (B). When inevitably the effects of the alcohol wear off, there are no adverse effects apart from being forced to accept reality as they originally perceived it. Individual ability to cope with this will vary and may well play a part in dictating our alcohol consumption, but it can be seen that the pattern will return to normal regardless of the quantity of alcohol consumed (Y,Z). This is not so in the case of the alcoholic (C). Here, consumption of the alcohol decreases the pain, but there is no longer a return to normality. The base position has now moved towards the pain area (X). As the disease progresses and X becomes the norm the amount

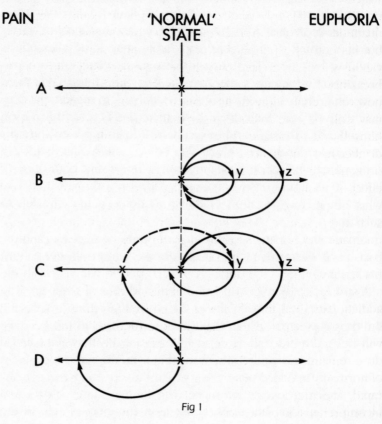

Fig 1

of drink previously required to attain state Z will now only achieve Y (as indicated by the broken line in C). Indeed Z can no longer be realised because the theoretical alcohol intake required would either be totally disabling or even lethal. The drinker is surprised by the relatively small initial effect of the alcohol and has to drink more and more before he feels 'normal' (D in Figure 1). This represents the stage at which the alcoholic tends to pass into acute and unannounced drunkeness. The alcoholic no longer becomes happy, he just gets drunk and this is not always appreciated either by the drinker or his associates. This is shown in Figure 2. It is not suggested that this is an effect which manifests itself immediately; it is a gradual situation which becomes more marked and more chronic as the disease progresses. Not only does the alcoholic now require increasing quantities of alcohol to reach the states (Y or Z) which he longs for, but his normal experience of life is becoming more untenable. A vicious circle is created, which he has increasing difficulty in breaking. The amount of drink originally producing euphoria is now required to allow the alcoholic to function at all. With drink he may only be able to cope superficially, and he is a risk both to himself and to others. There is no early warning system as the drinker had experienced previously, or as experienced by normal drinkers. The drinker is now surprised by the relatively small initial effect of alcohol and hence compelled to drink excessively to feel what he perceives to be normal. He experiences no euphoria as such and remembers very little apart from finding himself in some traumatic and horrific situation that can only be explained on the basis of his being drunk and incapable. No longer responsible for his actions.

A strong similarity can be found in the patterns of other forms of addiction. In the habitual taker of sleeping tablets the tolerance will build up to such an extent that the dose required to induce sleep will become perilously close to that causing death, for the lethal dose remains unchanged. The transition from the crude semblance of normality into incapacity, coma or even death can be exceedingly rapid, and the dosage differential frighteningly small. Hence the incomprehension of the alcoholic or drug addict. How did he or she

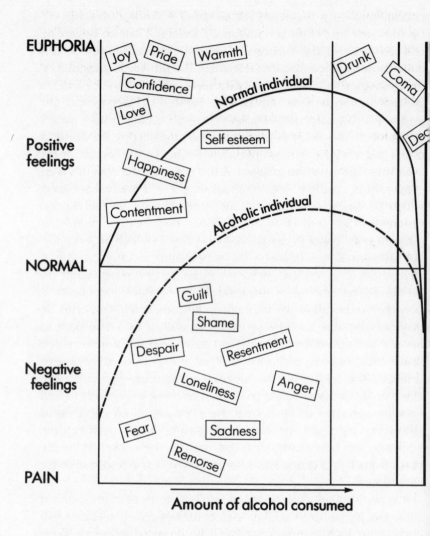

Fig 2 Effect of the amount of alcohol consumed on the normal and alcoholic individual. Euphoric or positive feelings are shown in the boxes above the normal baseline, pain or negative feelings below. In the normal, general well-being is improved until the amount consumed leads to intoxication. The advanced chronic alcoholic starts well below the normal base line, and requires a large quantity of alcohol to function normally. But that quantity is approaching that inducing intoxication.

get in that state? One minute apparently reasonably alright, the next oblivion and/or disaster. I know. I have experienced just that with the same incomprehension, fear and shame. And so have many others. What about the observers? From their standpoint they see somebody who no longer enjoys drinking but deliberately drinks themself into hideous situations, apparently regardless of the consequences. The drinker appears merely bewildered by the situation, which only adds insult to injury. Observers may attribute his behaviour to a decreased tolerance of alcohol, suspecting extensive liver damage. This is a possibility, but the more likely explanation is that the drinker, in his struggles to remove discomfort, has become even more devious in consuming vast amounts of alcohol and effectively concealing the fact. So both the drinker and those who have to watch him are equally baffled by this picture and what appears to be its illogicality.

It is, in fact, a simple and obvious pattern which as a problem could be considerably alleviated if understood by all parties concerned. At this stage there is no right or wrong, only a simple clinical pattern. The drinker is now fully in the grip of a hideous and destructive disease that no longer involves values or morality. In the early stages he may well have been forced to bend his own value system to accommodate his addiction, indeed had little alternative but to do so. But now it is beyond conscious manipulation. As we shall see, all defence mechanisms have now become as instinctive as those of a cornered animal and are equally justified.

These are the observable phenomena, and the phenomena experienced by the drinker in the crucial early and middle stages of the disease. We have suggested an explanation for the later stages, but can we find any further theoretical basis for this practical experience? For the answer I had first to think back some four years before my treatment at Broadreach to another disaster time, and another treatment but of a very different kind.

NEUROELECTRIC THERAPY (NET)

During a particularly distressing period of my life, the Rotary Club of Ashburton, my home town on Dartmoor in England, had, with exceptional kindness and compassion contributed money to send me for a revolutionary new Neuro-electrical treatment for alcohol and drug addiction supervised by Dr Karl Schmidt and Dr Meg Patterson in Somerset. The latter had pioneered the treatment and spent some twenty years evolving the technique. I have to admit that at the time I did not fully appreciate the significance of her work and, although understanding the underlying theory could not readily accept the empirical interpretations. Little faith, indeed.

In retrospect, I realised that the ten-day treatment had afforded me the longest period of sobriety (about fifteen months) until Broadreach. And it was relatively painless sobriety. Although Broadreach straightened out my thinking, even months after treatment I was suffering from what I can only assume to have been chronic withdrawal symptoms, considerable physical discomfort and occasional depression. This I could endure in the light of my new understanding, and I accepted that after years of alcohol and drug self-medication it would take time to re-adjust. All hope, but considerable pain. The reverse applied following the NET, no pain, but, as I see it now, little hope.

NET is now well established and is based on the evidence that the body produces its own natural defences against trauma, be it physical or mental. The substances responsible for these defences are naturally occurring opiates or endomorphins previously mentioned. The introduction of artificial pain reducing drugs allows them to some extent to take over the function of the natural opiates which as a consequence cease to be effective.

This mechanism can be visualised as follows. For the endomorphins to function they must first attach themselves to receptor sites in the brain, known as the benzodiazepine receptors. For various drugs it seems that their damaging effect results from their competition with the natural opiates for these receptor sites. If they become filled, for example with heroin, then they are no longer available for the endomorphins which in consequence cease to be produced. Benzodiazepine is the chemical basis of Valium which should say sufficient about the sedative actions and hazards of this drug.

Badawy speculates that in the case of alcohol, the benzodiazepine receptors may be occupied by the beta-carbolines (monamine oxidase inhibitors) formed by the interaction of acetaldehyde from the alcohol and the neurotransmitter serotonin, a similar reaction as postulated for the formation of TIQ.

Obviously, the accumulation of acetaldehyde resulting from a deficiency of the enzyme responsible for its breakdown as postulated by Dr Peters might potentiate the formation of these beta-carbolines. If the deficiency existed from birth as a result of a genetic error this might accentuate the destructive effect of alcohol in these individuals. If the deficiency resulted from alcohol abuse, it could also create a hypersensitivity to alcohol in those with a history of alcoholism.

This damage is masked by the anaesthetising effect of alcohol or the drug. All that is important to understand is that the natural defences are destroyed by alcohol or drug abuse. Whilst the body is being sedated by the drug this crucial damage will not be noticeable, but on removing that drug it becomes startlingly apparent as withdrawal symptoms. The body is emotionally naked, without defences.

NET involves the passage of small controlled frequencies of electrical charge through the brain, thereby restimulating the body to replenish its natural defences, the endogenous opiates or endomorphins. Using this technique the recovery begins immediately and most, if not all, of the distressing withdrawal symptoms are avoided. Thus it provides a vital tool for withdrawal.

It is now established that the endomorphin system can take as long as six months (heroin) to two years (alcohol and tranquilisers) to re-establish itself in the absence of NET. Two years in which we are liable to considerable physical pain and emotional stress. Either of these, if we have not been forewarned, can play crucial roles in relapses. After all, a few drinks and they seem to vanish. And we now know why.

I can see now that following NET I was well defended chemically, but unfortunately I continued to think along my old rigid patterns, and inevitably returned to drinking.

AN ALTERNATIVE APPROACH

The whole field of endogenous opiates and related compounds is expanding rapidly from the original isolation of enkaphalin in 1975. Recollection of the NET treatment and the role of endorphins caused me to re-examine the subjective phenomena reported on pages 41–45. The object was to fit as many of the observable or experienced phenomena associated with alcoholism into a rational theoretical framework. All I wish to present here is a simplified model which has the potential to explain most aspects of the development of a typical form of alcoholism from its benign inception to its catastrophic conclusion. I have inevitably borrowed from the observations of others and where appropriate, woven these into the fabric of my own experience and speculation.

THE TIQ MODEL RE-EXAMINED

There is no reason to doubt the evidence for an enzyme deficiency or the operation of the TIQ pathway in alcoholism, but whether this is a cause or an effect of alcoholism has yet to be ascertained. (See also p. 47.) I would also anticipate a more striking genetic pattern than is apparent if such a pathway were the cause, assuming this to be an inborn error of metabolism. For the same reasons, if alcoholics produced a highly addictive substance from their first drink, I would expect a much more rapid and profound deterioration, and extremely early loss of control. An enhancement of pleasure through an endomorphin like substance is a more attractive hypothesis. Further, why should there be considerable variations in incidence according to cultures, social classes, even occupations? Availability, temptation, stresses, yes, but if an all-or-none effect would this be so apparent?

For me, the familial nature of the inheritance would suggest that alcoholism is a secondary manifestation of some primary defect. The defect I see as that evidencing itself as an inherited personality trait, perhaps the elusive 'alcoholic personality'. The personality born literally of a chemical hypersensitivity, some imbalance in the natural defence-system resulting from a genetic flaw. A disturbance in, say, the neurotransmitter or endomorphin systems resulting in a less comfortable personality who finds, consciously or otherwise, that they can use alcohol or drugs to alleviate this discomfort. They then function more 'normally'. Alcohol or the drug is incorporated into their defence system, both literally in a chemical sense, and pyschologically. They anticipate the effect of a drink, recognise the need for a drink.

Providing there are no adverse side affects, then on a simple reward system they will continue to use alcohol and facilitate the development of alcoholism. The effect of the drink or drugs is to damage the natural defence of the body to stress. This creates a further need for drink or drugs. The victim is initially unaware of the damage as it will be masked by the sedative action of the drink or drugs. These conditions will elicit the picture described, increasing amounts of alcohol or drug being required to remove the increasing base discomfort.

Meanwhile a separate threat is being posed. As we have seen, the amount of alcohol required for normal functioning is becoming perilously close to that which will effectively inhibit larger areas of the central nervous system leading to loss of physical and mental co-ordination, coma and even death.

MINOR MISHAPS TO THE SUDDEN DRUNK

From my own experience and that of others, I believe this is the vital stage at which most alcoholics first question themselves. They have been aware that they drink heavily, but only after the occurence of some minor mishaps, perhaps social indiscretions or poor work

A–D

judgements, do they question the wisdom of their drinking. They make their first attempts to control their drinking and predictably fail to do so. In the absence of alcohol or a drug the full extent of the damage is revealed and normal functioning seems, or is, impossible. The only remedy is another drink. This is likely to lead to a classic bout drinking situation with repeated failed attempts to control the frequency of these bouts reflecting the desperation of the victim. The failure leads to guilt and shame, and the pattern of his drinking will become devious and defensive. The distinction between normality and near-coma becomes increasingly blurred as we have described; the sufferer passes from a semblance of normality into drunkenness or oblivion without apparent warning to himself or others. The unheralded black-out. It is this, I believe, that accounts for the ultimate bizarre, horrific and otherwise inexplicable events that punctuate the victim's later life.

We say it is a physical, mental and spiritual disease, yet we are suggesting it hinges on a chemical demand, no more. That is so, but this demand cannot go unheeded, and the victim of this addictive device must obey the command. This will take priority over every other value, social, legal or moral, and eventually over people. This first appears as minor transgressions that facilitate drinking, but then invades the very soul and elicits the shame that triggers off an entirely new game of defensive behaviour and deceit. All this time, as we shall see, the plumetting self worth is demanding the same solution. Drink. Or drugs.

This overall model helps explain many anomalies or uncertainties.

1 The familial nature of the disease
2 Social, cultural and occupational variations. Only a tendency is inherited which will be affected by environment, custom, availability or stress
3 Anyone can become an alcoholic by continual abuse of alcohol.
4 The range of alcohol problems. The extent of the predisposition will vary, as will environmental factors
5 Ineffectiveness of willpower.

6 Family background. Whether one or both parents suffer from alcoholism or other problems, the effect may not be environmental but suggest different manifestations of a common and inherited disorder

7 Progressive nature of alcoholism, both from the increasing chemical damage and the proliferating emotional problems

8 Unpredictability. It is alleged that the alcoholic is characterised by being unable to predict when the next drink will lead to disaster. This is unlikely on the all-or-nothing TIQ basis. It could be explained by changes in emotional states and the unheralded confusion.

9 Sudden drunkeness

10 Blackouts

11 Disastrous effect of tranquilisers, with or without alcohol

12 The tendency to cross addiction, alcohol and drugs

The drinker has no way of sensing or knowing the damage he is doing until the trap has been sprung. Without the knowledge provided here and in the following pages the sequence of events to follow is predictable and in that sense the alcoholic cannot be held responsible for the condition or its consequences, and should feel no guilt. He cannot halt a process he cannot hope to understand. But with understanding there is no further excuse. This understanding places responsibility back on the problem drinker, and on society and its attitudes.

Dr Meg Patterson, whose exciting pioneer work led to the development of NET, has contributed greatly to all areas of the understanding of addiction. Her book *Hooked* appeared during the preparation of this book, and is a testimony both to her scientific expertise and her compassion. Professor Kosterlitz and Dr Hughes of Aberdeen University, Scotland, have contributed greatly to our knowledge of endomorphins and their role in addiction.

Perhaps the most surprising feature of this work lies in its lack of general publicity given the seriousness of the problems. The average Briton, for example, has doubled his liquor consumption since the fifties, and the annual bill to the country for alcohol abuse has been estimated at £1,680 million, taking into account the cost of sickness, absence from work, hospital treatment, unemployment and premature death. A further £35 billion is actually spent on purchasing alcohol. In the United States, where there are an estimated 6 million alcoholics in a population of 220 million (UK 0.5 million in a population of 55 million) it is claimed that $25 billion is spent on drink-related problems. No doubt, similar statistics apply in other areas. According to *An Agenda for Action on Alcohol* published in 1986 (AAA, Livingston House, London) one in three drivers involved in road accidents is over the legal alcohol limit, half of those convicted for murder killed whilst under the influence of alcohol and drinking is linked to 52 per cent of deaths by fire, one third of all domestic accidents and 30 per cent of drownings. There is, nevertheless little general recognition that scientific research is offering a positive explanation of events, and potentially a chemical treatment for addiction. And the eventual importance of this research is relevant not only to addiction, I feel, but also our understanding of human behaviour in general and its problems.

Perhaps it salves the conscience of society to believe that alcoholics are born and totally different to others, or that the alcoholic knowingly sows the seeds of destruction, thus granting the rest seeming immunity. Do vested interests prefer an 'us-or-them' concept?

Let us now look at the associated emotional chaos, an equal part of the final disease.

3 Emotions

THE EMOTIONAL LIFE-SUPPORT MACHINE

In the previous chapter we have shown how an individual predisposed to the use of alcohol may develop a chemical dependency that is self-perpetuating, stress in its widest sense being the catalyst. Even in the absence of any apparent weakness, excessive and prolonged usage of alcohol or drugs will produce the same picture. Anyone can become an alcoholic if they try hard enough.

The drug 'crack', a form of cocaine, underlines this evidence dramatically. Described as addictive from the first smoke, the effect is briefer than that of cocaine but 'more intense than an orgasm, and when the user comes down he goes low, lower each time'. Here we have the ultimate 'super-drug' that for once is really frightening the users, demonstrating vividly and instantaneously the power of a chemical over the mind and body and its creation of an addictive demand. Yet this is only a dramatised version of the events occurring more insidiously in all chemical addiction.

NET will accelerate the repair of the chemical damage caused. Even without NET, providing the addict understands the cause for his acute and chronic discomfort and is prepared to endure this, nature will gradually carry out this same repair work. We are left, therefore with the question as to why, once this repair is accomplished does the recovered addict remain at risk and liable to relapses? We understand the self-perpetuating chemical basis of the disease, so what can we understand regarding the emotional implications, which as we shall see can be equally malignant. Just as in the case of the chemical dependency, much of their impact relies on our inability to recognise or understand them.

It is in these areas that the Minnesota Method is invaluable in that it forces us to re-examine ourselves, our motives and our values, examining our feelings and recognising how we use them in a destructive manner. It was this that inevitably led to my numerous relapses, unrecognised emotions leading to repetitive patterns of behaviour. The expertise and compassion of Broadreach House was necessary to draw this truth from me, and hundreds like me, before practical recovery could become a reality. The seeds of the approach were initially sown by Alcoholics Anonymous with their concept of a disease which affects people physically, emotionally and spiritually. The Minnesota Method is indebted to AA and actively encourages participation in their programmes, there being many parallels between the two both in theory and method. These concepts are being continually evolved by individual establishments who recognise their value, and their success relies on individual interpretation, integrity and commitment.

Our recovery depends on total understanding of the chemical, emotional and spiritual implications of the disease. I believe we can cope with that which we know and understand. Indecision and uncertainty are the hidden killers.

THE ALCOHOLIC PERSONALITY

The difficulties inherent in distinguishing between cause and effect as regards physical manifestations have been stressed, but they seem incredibly simple when the psychological implications are considered. The personality of the alcoholic has been dissected *ad nauseum* and although no doubt with good intentions, a far from pretty picture emerges. At the very least he is seen as self-centred, egoistic and immature, showing marked signs of development arrested early in childhood, sufficient to compel anyone to reach for the bottle. An example of how not to win friends and influence people except adversely! But just as the alcoholic is only diagnosed *after* he has become alcoholic, so the opportunity of studying accompanying personality traits only presents itself after the *effects* of alcoholism have become established. For the individual who is totally preoccupied with drink, who spends of necessity the larger part of his time arranging events, friends and finances to fit in with his drinking, the appearance of a degree of self-centredness would surprise no one!

Considering his alleged deficiencies I never cease to be astonished by the extraordinary degree of success, in its widest sense, enjoyed by many alcoholics prior to their eventual demise. 'He threw it all away' is the traditional lament, as is 'You would never believe it, he's so nice when he's sober'. Hence the tenacity of partners, clinging to the faith that the original will emerge once again, or the confession of a psychiatrist who told me she enjoyed working with alcoholics as they were such charming and interesting people when sober.

The existing personality of the alcoholic must reflect chemical domination: one of immediate gratification, child-like and self-centred and bearing no relation to the original. In general, retrospective and often highly selective analyses are suspect, all heroes having heroic backgrounds and all villains villanous ones!

We have suggested that in many cases some genetic aberration may produce an abnormality in response to stress, resulting in a prediliction for alcohol or drugs, and the need for these to attain normality rather than a high, a protection against hypersensitivity. An emotional overreaction to the environment could manifest itself in a variety of behavioural symptoms, both good and bad: not just apprehension and stress, but curiosity, imagination and creativity.

It has been suggested that immaturity is characteristic of any addiction, some proponents going so far as to suggest that in the extreme, emotional development is arrested from the onset of addiction. Although rather sweeping, I can see some sense in it. The addict finds a way to shield himself from much of the very experience which is essential to proper evolution, annihilating conflict rather than resolving it.

When I used alcohol to obliterate the spiritual and intellectual conflict surrounding my first sexual affair, I lost the vital opportunity of learning from that conflict. Certain emotional developments may be attenuated in the alcoholic or drug addict. What can we do about it?

SOCIALLY LEARNED BEHAVIOUR PATTERNS

Whether we have any pronounced character defect or not, various circumstances may precipitate a pattern of behaviour that unwittingly becomes fixed. Development and maturing should involve continuous revision or rejection of various patterns found to be workable at certain stages, but some patterns no longer of use can prove difficult to eradicate, being largely unrecognised. Some of these may operate at a subconscious level, affecting our behaviour inexplicably.

In discussing inherited personality traits in chapter 1, I referred to a period of obsessional behaviour occurring in early adolescence, the clarification of which may serve to illustrate these points. My previously idyllic schooldays were interrupted in the first year of grammar school by a year of horrendous victimisation by a particularly sadistic teacher. Both academically and socially my self-esteem was shattered and this led to a year when I was filled with sexual guilt which manifested itself in several different ways. I stress the sexuality and adolescent aspects as this illustrates that I was at a particularly receptive stage. Conventional psychiatry looked at the complexes and obsessional behaviour in isolation, and looked for the cause of the *sexual* guilt. In retrospect I can see that I was expressing anxiety through a channel appropriate to me at the time, reflecting the severely damaged self-image of the previous year. My confidence had been shattered by what I saw as authority.

The real importance and potential hazard of this not very remarkable experience is that I failed to understand it and for many years continued with an inexplicable, irrational fear of both failure and authority. I allowed myself to be dominated by a previous pattern of experience made all the more significant by its timing. Only through failure to recognise and understand it did I carry this burden through into my adult life, and allow it to influence my attitudes.

Neither these behavioural patterns nor our emotional quirks need be fixed, rigid, unalterable points of reference dictating the rest of our lives. We have to recognise them, 'own' them and decide what we wish to do with them. They form no more than a basis of experience from which we choose future paths. Eventually we must accept full responsibility for our feelings, for they cannot be forced on us unless we allow this to happen. The realisation and acceptance of choice of feelings is the essential key to eventual freedom for the addict. We need to take out our feelings, recognise and identify them. We need to know that only we are responsible for those feelings and equally we are responsible for the way in which they are deployed. We have to distinguish between the honest positive feelings and the perverted negative feelings, express the former and discard the latter, or reroute them appropriately. Only in this way can our personalities evolve creatively rather than destructively.

Equally we need to identify repetitive patterns of behaviour which no longer have relevance and may be damaging. Otherwise we may continue to follow them blindly without question, often to our detriment. The more we repeat these patterns, the more we reinforce them, readily becoming, for example, a scapegoat or dogsbody without real justification.

Certain patterns may be more comfortable because they remove the need for concrete decision making, for positive action or for confrontation. The addict achieves this through alcohol or drugs. We will see that in the later stages of alcoholism, bitterness, self-pity and resentment can readily be incorporated into patterns of behaviour conducive to drinking. Habits are basically addictive, comfortable and escapist, especially emotional or behavioural habits.

ATTITUDES

Real freedom is the recognition of the ability to change, and should be a constant challenge and delight. The excitement of being in control, of owning one-self is the opposite of addiction. At the same time as enjoying this freedom we must question the rigidity of some of our attitudes, formed initially from a synthesis of emotions and intellect but which can continue throughout our lives without revision. We come to see them as unalterable truths, when in fact we may well have outgrown the original debate on which they were founded, yet they will still dictate certain areas of our lives. Obvious areas are sex, morality, race, religion, politics and family role-playing. But if we care to look further we will see that unchanging attitudes affect a myriad of smaller areas from hygiene to Sunday trading. Start questioning. It is an exercise in freedom of choice.

YOUR LIFE STORY

It may be of interest and value to you to spend some time writing a personal life story, not an ego-trip or melodrama, both of which come easily to those of an alcoholic disposition, but a factual objective account, noting particularly those incidents or areas that affected general direction for good or bad, albeit transiently. Remember, your life did not begin with adolescence or a drink, although it may seem so. Go back as far as you can remember. Note particularly emotional responses to specific events and unsuspected behavioural patterns that are repeated. Taken in conjunction with your drinking pattern from chapter 1 this may provide invaluable clues to the roots of the problem, relating emotional states to drinking or drug abuse, anxiety, depression or euphoria. But most of all just learn both how life has treated you, and how you have treated life. It can be useful to discuss certain aspect with a really close and trusted friend, stimulating new thoughts on old topics, even allowing the surfacing of unsuspected feelings, motives and reactions. But do not allow them to influence you or be judgmental – remember, you own your feelings. Be honest and unbiased.

Leave plenty of space for additions or modifications. A convenient way of summarising the whole is to pick out the salient points, good and bad, and fit them to a 'snake' pattern of the type shown in Figure 3 the good on one side of the line, the bad on the other. Relate this to drink and drug abuse, both as cause and effect.

This exercise should allow you to look from the outside at the progression of both your life and your problem so far, and how the two are related.

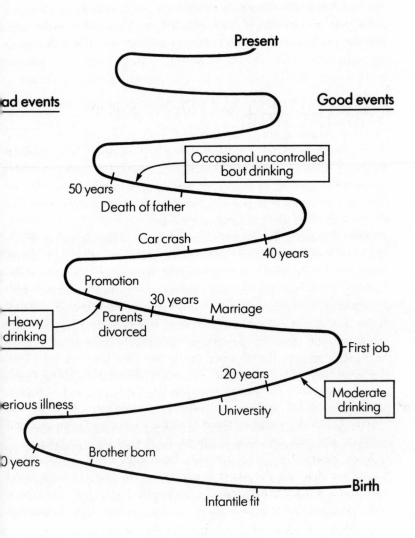

Present

Bad events

Good events

Occasional uncontrolled
bout drinking

50 years

Death of father

Car crash

40 years

Promotion

30 years   Marriage

Heavy
drinking

Parents
divorced

First job

20 years

Serious illness

University

Moderate
drinking

0 years

Brother born

Birth

Infantile fit

Fig 3

THE EMOTIONAL TRAPS_____

Ask yourself which emotions influence your drinking.

Include both those that may have led you to drinking in the first instance, as well as those that serve to perpetuate the condition.

ANXIETY, STRESS AND DEPRESSION_____

I tend to think of these as 'innocent precipitating factors', often predisposing us to using alcohol in the first place as some form of escape or defence. They are usually well recognised and can often be traced to rational causes. They would apply whether or not the individual suffered from, or was likely to suffer from alcoholism, to some extent providing justifiable excuses.

Quite obviously, should we inherit some weakness in our defence against stress, as we have postulated, then the effects of these emotions will be even more powerful. Further, as we have seen from the previous chapter, our defence mechanisms will become increasingly damaged during the progression of the disease. Indeed in the later stages our reasons for panic will no longer be justified, falling into the category of non-specific stress or anxiety, an almost permanent state in the absence of alcohol. We have, therefore, a classic picture of a somewhat insecure individual escaping from stress by the use of alcohol and by increasing the damage becoming dependent.

They are obvious reasons, they are logical reasons, and logic can be applied to discredit them as valid reasons for continuing drinking once alcoholism is presented. This does not underestimate their power, for they can be totally incapacitating, and the thought that they can be banished by a few drinks is very seductive.

Nevertheless, once the disease is established it is not difficult to accept that the degree of discomfort is relatively minimal compared with the horrendous results of the remedy! Further, once the chemical explanation of dependency is recognised the futility of the whole exercise can be rationally accepted, and the increase in confidence following a lengthy period of sobriety should convince the victim more readily than any theory.

In all respects the misapprehension at the basis of using drink or drugs to counteract states of stress and anxiety can be shown by rational discussion. It remains however the victim's choice whether or not he accepts this and whether he sees that a re-evaluation of self will be far more durable than the very transient and potentially disastrous crutch of alcohol or drugs.

ANGER, RESENTMENT AND SELF PITY_____

In contrast to the innocent precipitating factors described above, the second area demanding attention comprises the 'devious and malignant factors', and I have chosen the phrase carefully. The principal components are anger, resentment and self-pity.

They are devious inasmuch as we may well not recognise their presence, and even should we do so we are unlikely to accept the extent of their damaging role unless we fully understand the mechanisms involved. Yet one or all of them is usually responsible for the sinister emotional overlay which provides an ever-present excuse to continue to drink when all knowledge, wisdom and experience dictates otherwise. And being unseen the enemy is all the more dangerous, eluding conventional defences, and taking us unawares.

These emotions are malignant in that initially they may appear to be no more than an irritating intrusion on the fabric of our thinking, yet in time they can overwhelm and subordinate all other thoughts and feelings, allowing a rigid pattern of behaviour to become established, which continuously seduces us back to the bottle.

All these three, together or independently, may be present before the onset of alcoholism and may precipitate it, predisposing us to seek escape or defence through alcohol or drugs, at a less conscious level than stress, anxiety or depression. The victim may be aware of isolated episodes where they manifest themselves but rarely of the continuing effects for they operate subtly through a variety of disguises.

Their role in perpetuating addiction is even more sinister, and to appreciate the full implications we need to review the whole addiction-emotional cycle.

In Chapter 8 we will discuss self-esteem and the vital need to re-build this badly damaged asset in recovery. When dependency is first acknowledged, the addict cannot help but be overwhelmed with guilt, and accordingly his self-esteem will shrink, all the more so as he has no explanation for his inability to control his drinking. It represents to him a personal failure, most likely a lack of will-power and an inability to order his life correctly, for he has no knowledge of any disease concept.

As a result of this diminished self-esteem the addict is compelled to build up an elaborate system of emotional and practical defences in order to protect his self-esteem and conceal his guilt. These are discussed in Chapter 5, but suffice it here to mention denial, minimising, and rationalisation, excusing, lying and blaming.

Although these are aimed at protecting his image by concealing the problem, he is aware of most of them, and bitterly ashamed. They dramatically cut across all his previously cherished values, and run counter to his previously held self-image. Thus the very item he wishes to protect is damaged further in his own assessment, and a vicious circle ensues. The emotional ramifications and reper-cussions of this plummeting self-esteem are enormous, including feelings of imperfection, rejection and resentment of himself, of drink, his condition and the way he sees himself to be judged by society. Self-pity and anger are obvious corollaries, although the latter is rarely expressed correctly (see below).

These three together with the guilt, shame and sense of worthlessness are not only results of the drinking, but also provide an excuse for drinking. The effects become causes, thus perpetu-ating the disease from an emotional standpoint. And this we have to add to the chemical self-perpetuating mechanism that we now understand. And before very long his pathetic defences are no longer adequate, and society demonstrates its disapproval.

By this time he is likely to be totally preoccupied with the problem, obsessed by either drinking or not drinking. The chemical demand and the emotional confusion fill his whole world, effectively strangling all his real and honest feelings. There is no room for these and inevitably they atrophy. His entire value-system and his beliefs (see chapter 8) are eventually eroded by the all-demanding drug.

This is the cruellest aspect of the disease. The chemical and emotional destruction will continue unchecked bringing in its wake the inevitable tragedies and catastrophies, the drug-induced disease demanding more of the drug and meanwhile robbing the victim of any semblance of dignity, respect, or self-respect. The only difference is that he is aware of his total powerlessness whereas other people are not. The distress, hopes and fears of those he loves cause very deep and damaging pain, and any sanctimonious judgement creates great bitterness. Is it surprising that he retreats increasingly into his private hell?

Although it should be obvious that a variety of different emotions are now contributing to the addictive process, the true significance of the trio of anger, resentment and self-pity is that they operate largely on an unconscious level, particularly the first two, and remain unrecognised.

Equally, we fail to recognise the deterioration in our remaining honest feelings. This deterioration results not only from lack of room in which to exercise them, but also from their failure to be condoned or to elicit any response. The right of the alcoholic to love, even to feel angry or happy, is continually questioned both by him and by others. It is generally considered that he has abdicated any rights to real emotions, and unfortunately he eventually does just that. Our real feelings die at the expense of parasitic negative feelings of supressed anger, resentment and self-pity. These now dictate a macabre game of cause and effect, stimulus and response, the final effect of which has to be our total destruction. Every stage in the decline is calculated to reinforce the inevitability.

The alcoholic may well have conned those around him for years, yet this is trivial compared to the way in which he has conned himself. He no longer *owns* his own feelings; irrational and unrecognised excuses endorse immediate and transient gratification

– temporary relief from a private hell – with no thought to the eventual and inevitable collossal loss. Ill-assorted feelings run riot as a result of the alcohol, thus affording some relief, a violent and spasmodic emotional masturbation. An emotional spending spree with a very uncompromising bank manager demanding emotional and spiritual bankruptcy.

The real person is dead. A shell remains, a shell designed to permit continued drinking and to fractionally extend a largely futile existence. For the real person *is* the feelings. It is those feelings that stimulate or respond to our environment; that determine our hopes and despairs; that define our honesty and provide our values, our knowledge of love, our commitment to life. But there is no longer room in which to exercise them.

Yet whatever the views on the body, there can be no doubt that the spirit that has died can assuredly be resurrected. And finding again the real you, whatever the stage of your alcoholism, is an exciting adventure and is immensely rewarding not only to yourself but to those around you. You will also have time to discover them, as well! No longer a helpless observer of the inevitable but an active, excited participant in life.

FEELING ANGRY

Well, we have attended the funeral and noted the promise of resurrection. For those well versed in such matters, it may seem unreasonable to have grouped anger along with resentment and self-pity under the banner of negative emotions. It is of course, for anger well expressed is a positive and healthy feeling. We are really referring to perverted anger, that is, anger which is improperly expressed. This can appear in all manner of disguises such as anxiety, depression or within a more complex framework of obsessions, compulsions or phobias. Physically it may elicit itself as unreasonable fatigue, or a variety of psychosomatic symptoms ranging from mild headaches to hysterical paralysis. The real problem appears to be to exclude symptoms rather than enumerate them. We commonly talk of tension or an emotional 'well' and such phrases are useful in visualising the emotional frustration leading to perversion. If a buildup of emotion cannot be released through an appropriate outlet then it will seek other outlets. These present the diverse symptomology. At the same time, the stimulus eliciting the emotion is not satisfied, as it would be by the normal expression of that emotion, and hence continues to demand attention. Acute symptoms become chronic. Eventually such an emotional imbalance will reflect itself in physiological disturbances, creating the psychosomatic picture. We enter the realms of target organs or target emotions, where it is suggested that in certain individuals there are weak spots. Thus one individual experiencing stress may be aggressive and have an ulcer whereas another is pathologically shy and suffers head-aches.

Whatever our subconscious choice, we are faced with a situation in which we become conditioned to emotional displacement along specific channels, with no hope of satisfying the original feeling. The situation becomes chronic. If we attempt to 'treat' the overt symptom we will find that at best the treatment is only palliative, or more likely, if the symptom is removed, the basic frustration will appear elsewhere.

For example, supposing we feel angry at life in general, but we do not recognise this and show that anger. The well of anger finds an outlet in insomnia. We take sleeping pills to alleviate the condition. Unfortunately, although we now sleep, we suffer from headaches, but not to worry, we can take aspirin. There is little doubt that if this proves effective some other bizarre symptom will appear.

A quarter bottle of Scotch, or whatever your medicine or dosage, will effectively banish all symptoms – until the alcoholic liberation or anaesthesia has worn off. Certainly it allows the alcoholic to express his feelings to the full, which he frequently does by either physical or verbal violence. And it also relaxes him both mentally and physically, as well as deadening discomfort. If it were not often immediately embarrassing and ultimately fatal, alcohol would, in this respect, represent a universal panacea! Indeed, that is exactly what it does represent to the unhappy and uncomfortable alcoholic.

A–E

But whether sleeping tablets and aspirin, or alcohol, be the chosen remedy, the original problem, anger in this case, remains. It is not difficult to see how treatment with mood-altering chemicals can become a way of life, a life of addiction.

There is good reason to emphasise the importance of anger. It is surrounded by misconception. It is assumed, wrongly, invariably to be a violent emotion, associated with hatred and is often equated with ill-temper, but this is denying the acceptance of a normal, rational and healthy emotion having a specific function. Why do we tend to supress it?

Often we fear that we will lose control. But here, again, we are thinking of temper rather than anger. Joy and anger are fundamental expressions of feeling exhibited universally from birth. What other ways has a baby of communicating its oneness or not with the world? Anger invariably becomes 'losing one's temper' if the anger is only released after being bottled up. Perhaps we fear the effect will be too destructive on the victim. This is an immature approach showing little understanding. A true relationship will only grow if differences are aired, and causes of friction explored. Not to do so is to build on the shifting sands of non-stated values.

This also applies to a fear of rejection which often results in stifled anger. If we are to form valuable relationships we have to take risks, to respect each others value systems, even if we cannot wholly share them.

A fear of hurting or even destroying the other person is another excuse, but this attitude is, in fact, diminishing that person. Why should we assume we have that power?

Lastly, of course, there is often fear of retaliation. This casts doubt on the validity of one's own convictions and consequent anger. We are now doubting our ability to handle other people's feelings.

Anger is an honest feeling that should be respected. First it has to be recognised, and then acknowledged or 'owned'. 'It is my feeling and I am responsible for that feeling.' It is then necessary to do something with that feeling. Express it, preferably in a concise and inoffensive manner. By that, we do not mean any withholding or dilution of the anger, but an honest confrontation.

'You make me feel angry' is a common accusation and totally unjustified. No one can make you feel anything. You cannot be made to feel guilty or ashamed. You *own* your feelings and they are yours to do with as you wish. This gives you responsibility, yet makes you less vulnerable. Confrontation means 'I feel angry because . . .' not 'You make me angry . . .' Do not add insult to injury by blaming your feelings on someone else. This is ascribing motives to the other person, being judgemental.

But most important, express your feeling of anger, and why you feel anger, *at the time of the experience.* Feel it, own it, express it, immediately. Honest polite confrontation, respecting the other person. Forget, 'I should feel angry . . .' or 'I am sorry, I feel angry but . . .' Either you are angry or you are not.

Since you have probably grown accustomed to a lifestyle characterised by denial of one sort or another, it is likely that you have skipped lightly through the preceding pages in the confidence that, although your faults be manifold, repressed anger is not your particular scene. Certainly a lie, for everyone is guilty to some extent, alcoholic or not. The list of disturbing physical and emotional complaints resulting from frustrated or perverted anger is legion, many of them being familiar accompaniments to living that we accept without question. From finger drumming and twitches, through a variety of behaviour such as icy politeness, controlled precise speech, obsessional actions, or 'martyrdom', even leading to physical aches and pains and that much-discussed area, impotency. To deny that you experience frustrated anger would be to deny your membership of the human race, with its normal share of ills.

The analogy of an old stove is often drawn. If the chimney is blocked, then smoke leaves from a variety of chinks which is inefficient and not good for the fire. Our emotional flue is well and truly blocked.

If we are hurt but do not express anger, one of the most likely and powerfully destructive emotions we may experience is that of resentment. The role of this in the alcoholic's or addict's decline cannot be over estimated, so look at yourself most carefully, for resentful you probably cannot help but feel.

RESENTMENT: A REAL KILLER

Resentment is the king of blind-alley negative feelings. It has no proper expression and can remain incubating, or more appropriately, smouldering within us for a life time. The various forms of resentment can dictate a whole way of life. They are rarely recognised and the original causes are often buried deep. And there is no stronger power compelling us to seek refuge in alcohol.

Check yourself for resentments, and check yourself most carefully, for as with anger you may well conclude initially that you have none. Take time with paper and pencil to note down resentments that you are aware of experiencing. You can be sure that there will be many of which you are unaware. Go back as far as your memory can take you, and do not minimise. It is quite extraordinary how guilt will refuse to allow us to admit to resentments, even though a true understanding of these is essential to recovery. Your very reluctance underlines their importance. Where applicable, discuss them with someone close to you whose opinion you can trust, especially your family, for they may be able to highlight the true resentment more clearly.

A common failing when checking for negative feelings, or for that matter any fault, is to deny their existence *before* the onset of the problem. This is, in part, associated with the obsessive perfectionism of the alcoholic. We can blame a lot on alcohol but not everything! It is quite possible we were not perfect before we started drinking – like the rest of the human race! Try joining it please.

At the same time, it is apparent that alcohol itself will, and should give rise to many good reasons for harbouring resentments, and these nurture the disease itself.

You have good cause for resenting alcohol – for the demands it imposes on you, for what it does to you. You may well have reasons to resent what it has done to your domestic life, your social life or your work. Or perhaps you resent other people's attitudes to your drinking, even those of your bank manager. No, you will not be short on current resentments. But, nevertheless, make sure you differentiate these from those resentments which formed before you started drinking or which would have occurred without the dubious benefit of alcohol. An old school happening, desertion by friend or lover, a spiteful aunt, loneliness or desertion in childhood, and so on. Or even something physical. Check whether they have been responsible for establishing any patterns of behaviour which you now unwittingly follow. Take them. Own them. Expose them fully and gain your freedom. What right have they to control the rest of your life? You have greater strength than that.

Then examine with particular care those resentments you presently harbour, and try to see how they participate in drinking patterns. How often do you preface a drink with the thought 'Oh, what the hell . . .' or 'It can't be worse . . .', 'Why bother . . .', 'What's the use . . .', and a host of other clichés which suggest that you may as well drink. Was it the domestic or work row which led you to that drink, was it recriminations over that tiny little drink which led to the excessive bender, or was it self-pity, 'Nobody cares'?

There will be no shortage of resentments, but let us go a little deeper into this. There are the immediate ones of the 'Look what life has done to me . . . it's not fair' variety, but there are also more subtle ones that we often fail to associate directly with alcohol.

One of the most important of these concerns the inescapable fact that our drinking affects the behaviour of those around us, particularly those with whom we hope to give and receive love. It is almost certain that love born of a faint heart in the first place will scarcely survive the assault. But fortunately love can be remarkably stubborn and unflinching. Nevertheless, for sheer survival, your partner may well remove themselves from you to some extent, or possibly (how dare they!) interfere in some way with your drinking/ finances/spare time/friends. It is not difficult to envisage resentments emanating from what you might see as an unjust change in marital climate! You may see your partner as domineering, interfering, remote or downright frigid.

A similar picture may be reflected with less intimate relationships. 'My kids don't respect me' or 'Why don't they give me more responsibility at work?', or 'Fred never talks to me at the pub these days'.

Little has been said of self-pity as it needs little explanation, and its destructive effects are obvious. The triggering events may be real or imaginary, but always heavily dramatised. It may even become a more or less normal state of mind, with only minor fluctuations. This is particularly dangerous as, once again, it may have no specific cause and not be immediately recognised. Quite obviously it relates to both anger and resentment and adds to a deep sense of unworthiness.

THE EMOTIONS OF RECOVERY

The reasons for relapsing after either short or long periods of sustained sobriety are obvious, for removal of alcohol only allows free play of the original emotional problems. What better excuse for resuming drinking? Especially as long practice has taught you the efficacy of this treatment. The need to drink is now even more urgent than initially. Your inability to cope emotionally is enhanced by the chemical damage resulting from the alcohol, and your environment (friends, family, work), are damaged by your behaviour. Frustrated emotion, chemical damage and adverse circumstances make a pretty powerful cocktail!

THE 'DRY DRUNK' SYNDROME

You may also suffer from what is called the 'dry drunk syndrome'. This means behaviour resembling that of the drinker but which occurs during lengthy periods of sobriety. The most common feature is acute mental and/or physical uncoordination. From what we now know of the chemical damage and the time taken for repair, the physical side of this is immediately understandable. But emotional complications will also continue to operate unless treated. A very good friend of mine did in fact attend Broadreach some three years after stopping drinking in order to sort out his emotional confusions. He had attained sobriety only in the sense of no longer using alcohol, but recognised this was not sufficient to ensure serenity. AA insist on a continued programme of rehabilitation on an emotional and spiritual basis, a principle endorsed also by Patterson.

It is for these reasons that it is vital that the recovering alcoholic learns to *recognise* and *own* his feelings. Whatever disturbing emotion I experience these days I make, when appropriate, a conscious effort to identify that emotion and its likely cause. An 'uneasy' feeling, or one of non-specific depression can often be traced to some anger or resentment for example. By finding a rational basis I find I can cope much more readily with the feeling, even dismiss it as inconsequential, or take appropriate remedial action. It can be a very important exercise and its efficiency can only increase with practice.

Now that you have stopped drinking, why is life not perfect? Here we have the classic problems whenever an alcoholic signs the pledge. Surprisingly, even for the non-alcoholic, life does not always go exactly as he or she wishes, and one can guarantee that for the recently dried-out alcoholic it very rarely does. Unfortunately, only the alcoholic recognises the magnitude of his efforts in struggling towards sobriety. Most other people, not unreasonably, see no more than that he has stopped drinking, no Herculean task in their eyes, and not before time. They certainly do not see it as giving carte blanche to be entirely self indulgent in every other way.

Life might be very bad for the drinking alcoholic, but that does not imply it is all good in sobriety. The normal 'slings and arrows of outrageous fortune' continue to rain but the ability to meet these is part of the recovery, or put another way, the inability to meet them was contributory to the disease.

Moreover, and most importantly, it is likely that your dramatic resolution followed a very prolonged period of unsatisfactory and destructive behaviour. For much of this time you were relatively sheltered from the horror of the reality by alcoholic anaesthesia. Those around you, particularly your partner or the person closest to you, were exposed to the full blast, with no insulation and no escape. Few people can be as devastatingly cruel and critical as the practising alcoholic. They fight with the ferocity of a cornered animal, their emotional flood-gates are opened and a torrent of pent-up feelings is released. The alcoholic may well have felt his attack is justified, in fact long overdue. (There is a grain of truth in this, albeit a microscopic one, but had he possessed the ability to express his anger appropriately and at the right time, that situation would not have arisen.) In desperation his attack was aimed at annihilating the enemy rather than confronting it. It was total war, with no convention to license the armoury!

Not surprisingly, you can rarely recall the true vehemence of your attacks, or the horrific content of your abuse. Should this be drawn to your attention, you expect total and immediate forgiveness. This underestimates the recipients of this colourful abuse. They may well accept that superficially it was alcohol speaking, but they cannot dismiss the possibility that your behaviour was based on a belief within yourself.

Unfortunately, all too often your criticism may not have been transacted on a personal level. Fearing it to fall on deaf ears, the alcoholic will resort to any captive audience, with scant regard to the reception his 'confidence' will receive. This, perhaps, is the most wounding of all to those closest to you, particularly as it will usually be the opposite sex who responds when you adopt the 'misunderstood' guise.

The damage you have done will be considerable and a massive repair job is required to restore that vital element of any relationship, trust. The current attempt at sobriety may well not be the first, and others' hopes may have been shattered, once or many times. Is it surprising that your partner needs time, considerable time, for reassurance, time to build up *their* confidence in your sincerity.

The material damage will vary but is likely to extend at least into finances, and possibly into property and lost status. To all these troubles and their numerous ramifications can be added those relating to a very real change in your partner's role. They may, of necessity, have become an altogether harder person and of considerably greater independence. Perhaps they have had to fend for themselves, make many major decisions, even make new friends. Should they now sacrifice all they have built with time and energy, not to mention initiative, and throw their future entirely back on your far-from-guaranteed mercy? Chop up the lifeboat and jump back on the ship that may still sink? We ask too much of our partners.

If we have destroyed much, then we have a great deal to rebuild, and the most delicate and important component of a relationship is trust, being able to rely on someone, having total confidence in that person, and in a really good relationship, so much more, almost akin to faith itself. Trust involves sharing, mutual acceptance and understanding. It is the total vulnerability of naked lovers, who know their vulnerability will not be exploited. It is not the 'blind love' of falling in love, or of infatuation, for in reality this is irrational with no foundation in experience. Real trust is painstakingly acquired over long experience and with very deep knowledge and insight into the other person. There is no way, from what we have said, that the practising alcoholic deserves trust.

When trust has been damaged, the length of time required for its repair will be relative to the damage. Your partner needs time to recognise you again, to acknowledge again the qualities previously associated with you, and to have confidence that they are now constant. This demands a great deal of patience from you but will be justified. To trust and be trusted is a very basic human need, the essential security and comfort for which we all long, but rarely fully attain. It is a measure of considerable success for the recovered alcoholic when he senses that trust has been returned to him.

To return to resentment, you may wonder why you still feel this, now that you have stopped drinking. You resent those things that have not been immediately returned to you, and you resent those things that have changed in your absence – for absence it was. Because the newcomer to sobriety is truly contrite, then he expects the immediate and unconditional return of those 'goods' that he sees as 'confiscated' during his drinking. His is the immediate punishment and reward psychology.

In early phases of the game his partner may be more than willing to play the expected role to convince him that this is a far better way of life. But we operate more subtly than Pavlovian dogs. We are more sophisticated and we see many ways of killing the proverbial cat. So the partner should be cautious of this approach. Continued learning with gradual and probably unconscious reward will build the strongest foundations for recovery.

The ex-drinker has no doubts about his continuing sobriety, having just emerged from a private hell to which he has no wish to return, and assumes this is recognised by everyone else. So, where is the love and affection? The all-giving blissful joy and sharing? The immediate rapport? He resents the coolness, interpreting it as indifference. He resents the watchful eye or the caution with money. Depending on the extent of your previous withdrawal from your partner's life, they may have had cause to establish meaningful relationships elsewhere and not only of their own sex. She or he may have needed advice, or comfort and the opposite sex may have proved more convenient for both these needs. Heaven forbid, they may have needed just company or even fun, or, dare we say, escape? If your withdrawal was lengthy they may even have replaced that which they had lost. We all hope for affection and love. And why should you assume that you were the only one feeling lonely and lacking in self-worth?

SEX

The importance of our sex life to our ego is dramatically underlined by the extraordinary reluctance of many alcoholics to accept that their sex life has suffered to any appreciable extent. They may brag about failures in every other department of their lives, but when it comes to sex they confine themselves to reckless sexual adventures and indiscretions, usually, and with good reason, stopping short of 'the act'. For that is precisely where they always stop short.

I would not suggest that every male alcoholic suffers from impotency, but he is substantially more at risk than his colleagues. But, let us admit it, he can be a pretty lousy lover. And a few occasions of lousy love-making can do much to destroy the fundamental pattern of sexual love. She has lost her basic trust in you. She is never sure who you are. She fears that she may be a mere gratification, similar to the bottle. Most of all, she fears that she is less important than the bottle.

To add to all this, your sex lives have become sporadic and unpredictable, to depend on *your* emotional and physical well-being, and largely neglecting your partner's. There may be times when they seriously doubt if they like you, let alone love you. And a far-from-subtle smell of alcohol serves as a constant reminder of all these doubts at the most vital time. Not good. You may, when you wish, be full of charm, you may be extraordinarily romantic, citing the bards at length. Hopefully, you love your partner to distraction. But your love life, witness your performance in bed, is almost certainly lacking, and possibly a dead loss. And deep down you know it. Assuming all this, can you doubt that your partner may be reluctant to immediately share sexual excesses with you. A little doubt, slight frigidity, even downright abhorrence may prevail for a while. Should you have reason to doubt their fidelity at all times, question what effect this has on you, and your sex life. It may help you understand.

With not a thought for these explanations, how you burn with resentment at your partner's coolness or indifference. Totally wrapped up in your own problems you have no time to consider theirs. Of course you want to be happy again, but have you thought how you damaged their happiness, or how often. Start working on the whole relationship, as described in the next chapter.

Finally, in his struggle to maintain sobriety, the ex-alcoholic is compelled to see with painful clarity the effect drinking has had on other aspects of his or her life. Perhaps the lower status job, the smaller car or the lost licence, the second mortgage, perhaps just the look on the face of the bank manager. In fact, the concrete cost of the drinking. More resentment. More falling self-esteem. If he does suspect his wife has had an illicit affair he has a ticket to ride on: forgetting he has been away, forgetting the real cause of this chaos, alcohol, and seeing only the effect. He asks that his past misbehaviour should be forgotten, dismissed as a product of alcohol not himself. Yet he rarely has the tolerance, humility and compassion to concede that these circumstances and the motivations of those concerned are equally a result of drink.

In recovery, therefore we are threatened by two highly dangerous situations, one a destructive emotional sickness, the other an addictive chemical demand and hyper-awareness of emotional trauma. Even with the benefit of NET we still have the emotional confusion to cope with. There is always a reason for our emotions, and the actual emotion may not be the one we register. Only by correctly identifying the emotion and by honestly acknowledging the reason can we adapt and evolve. Remember, identify, accept, own, and express appropriately.

4 Relationships

Contrary to what we may often feel, we are *not* alone. Whether we like it or not, we are all part of one big, not necessarily happy family with whom we are supposed to integrate and relate. Encouragement to 'rejoin the human race' implies a two-way contract in which the object is not solely that you reap the benefits.

Although much of what we will discuss will relate to the conventional family with specific reference to the husband and wife relationship, it should not deter those who do not find themselves in this precise relationship from reading further. Most of what is said is applicable equally, with only a minor shift of emphasis, to any relationship in which the alcoholic or addict is involved. Obviously the degree of passion, the emotional intensity of the relationship, will dictate the extent of the role it plays in the disease. Further, I should stress that in describing any events or motives I am attempting to build a general model with which one of the partners may be able to identify to some extent. It is not intended to suggest that such situations necessarily do, will or are likely to occur in specific instances.

Assuming that a relationship operates reciprocally, it is apparent that we have to consider both the effects of the partner on the disease, as well as the very unhappy effects of the disease on the partner. On the surface, it does seem that the emotional traffic is essentially one way, but this is not so.

WHY WE ARE SO DESTRUCTIVE

Unless what follows is fully understood, then no matter how well intended the partner, no matter how much they love the victim, no matter what approach they adopt, they will continue unwittingly to aid and abet the disease. It is for this reason that most modern approaches to the disease insist on family psychotherapy, involvement of husband, wife, children or parents in the process of understanding the problem, and learning about the part they should play. We have discussed the need to own our feelings and not to be judgemental of others motives. This applies particularly to the alcoholic and his or her partner, for the former is hyper-sensitive and the behaviour of the latter often affected by the considerable pressures under which they live. Let it be clear that the main motive of a partner who stays with an alcoholic has to be that of love for the very person that alcohol threatens to eclipse, and a faith that eventually that real person will re-emerge.

In the beginning of this book I used the word 'contagious' in describing alcoholism. I was not suggesting that those caught up in the immediate surrounds of the alcoholic would necessarily reach for a bottle, although such an impulse is understandable and unfortunately possible. Assuming the partner is immune to the most overt symptom, he or she will, if not helped, inevitably be deeply infected with the emotional sickness. Almost without exception however this will be denied by them. 'Who me? Don't go playing psychiatrist with me.' After all, who keeps the world going whilst the other is away? And therein lies the whole story. The partner generally starts by maintaining a workable world around the alcoholic, and after varying periods of time is compelled to change strategies abruptly (and to the consternation of the alcoholic) and start building a new world around themselves. Their protective shell. During the entire process and its evolution they have to convince themselves that their motives are altruistic and done solely out of interest for the alcoholic. And to a substantial extent they are, but increasing contamination clouds their own judgement and self-analysis. Their very denial that they too are ill draws a dramatic parallel with the attitude of the alcoholic, a parallel which follows through each stage.

IN THE BEGINNING

Remember. In exactly the same way as the alcoholic struggles to deny that he is ill, or that he has a problem, so will the partner. If not literally, then in the form of a 'don't think about it and it will go away' philosophy. Why not? It is a very unhappy situation for them as well. They have heard, or even seen what alcohol can do, just how destructive it can be. It is a considerable cross to bear. They certainly do not wish it on their partner, nor do they wish it on themselves. It is going to take all their courage to face it eventually; it will push their love to the limits of endurance.

I say this to the alcoholic. You are ill, you are not responsible for your disease, so do not indulge in needless guilt or self-recriminations. But never underestimate the stresses imposed on your partner by that disease. If you ever have cause to doubt their behaviour, remember the pressures and the fundamental cause, your alcoholism. And the greater the bond of love, the greater the effect the disease will have on them. If it has no effect, then you must settle for indifference. You have to be as compassionate to them as you hope the world will be in judging you. When sober, you will have a very big and demanding task, take on this mantle of responsibility eagerly. Not with sorrow for the past, but strength for the future.

In the early days, exactly as the alcoholic will be showing an increased tolerance to drink, so the partner will be showing an increased tolerance to his drinking. There may be no undue behaviour problems, but the drinking is increasing, possibly stretching finances a little. But he is happy and entitled to rest after a hard day, and has every right to spend his own money – all said in the name of love. Just as in his case, she doesn't *want* to know exactly how much he drinks or spends. What is it to do with her? This denial will gradually encompass minor indiscretions at work or play, even to the extent of preferring to believe that he is ill, and therefore will not go into work, rather than accepting the reality that he is suffering from a hangover. Although not quite as total, she experiences her own variety of 'black-out' – consciously in her case, putting certain happenings out of her mind. She doesn't want to know that he has made a fool of himself. He has alcohol to assist convenient amnesia, she hasn't. And because she loves him, she assumes, incredibly wrongly, that he knows what he is doing, and she has no right to interfere.

THE DISEASE SPREADS

Eventually she concedes that he definitely drinks too much, yet again develops exactly parallel defences as his. She finds excuses: overwork, stress, anxiety, depression. That is why he drinks. Around this stage some damage occurs, damage to his work life or damage to their social lives, or even to their relationship. He has a problem.

Having accepted that he has a problem, the real nature of which eludes her, the insidious 'preoccupation' phase arises and will remain with her. More and more of her energies are directed to his problem. These take the form of covering up for him, tidying for him, adapting her life to fit in with his problem. And, of course, looking after him if he is ill, and talking through his problems. The problem is talked through with minimal honesty on both sides. The intentions are good, but neither can voice their real fears, and immediately and falsely face the future together with misplaced determination and new hope. Both of them are by now living a life a large part of which revolves around drink. Other matters are increasingly excluded. They have both become preoccupied with the problem.

THE ENABLER

She has already played this role in her 'tidying' efforts but now it demands a large part of her time and energy. Not understanding the true nature of the disease any more than he does, the emphasis is on controlling the drink, or more correctly, avoiding the excess. Even more, avoiding the repercussions of the excess. He is under enough strain without having to telephone work to say he is ill; she does it. He has no time to answer those letters or, more likely, bills. She does it. He does not want to bother about that friend/enemy/party/candle-lit dinner/meeting/holiday – she will cancel it or re-arrange it. In fact she will re-arrange every aspect of life to conceal the problem of his drink both from the outside world and themselves. All this facilitates his drinking, shielding him from adverse affects.

THE DECLINE

It is not always clear, that in 'Game playing' we are not aware of the roles we play and how we use them for our own ends. In the present situation both the rescuer and the victim gain some satisfaction from their roles, the rescuer by being of use and involved with the problem, the victim by gaining sympathy (as well as being able to continue drinking). He may well be manipulating the rescuer, compelling both to stick to their allotted places. Nevertheless, there is a limit to his enjoyment of the victim role, and his own guilt or shame will turn into resentment against the rescuer. He may object to her interference, or more strongly voice some belief that she is responsible for his drinking. He thus changes to the role of persecutor, transferring his guilt to her.

THE FALL

Sooner or later she has to accept that she cannot influence his drinking, and considerable anger and resentment creeps into the relationship. She can only conclude that he 'loves the bottle more than her', a pretty devastating revelation, and deeply humiliating. The word should be 'needs', not 'loves', of course, but even so it is not easy to understand the difference unless one happens to be an alcoholic.

Another curious parallel now comes into existence. He *should* be able to accept that he is powerless over alcohol (see Chapter 1) and she, accepting this, *should* be able to see that she is equally powerless. Neither, did they but know it, have any reason to feel ashamed. But, because of lack of understanding of the problem, self-worth is falling on both sides, leading to considerable anger and mutual resentment. Feelings are being stifled and this leads to further stress and anxiety. Both are emotionally sick and stand no chance of relating to each other properly.

It is usually at this stage that she changes her enabling approach to one of threats or promises. Her promises ('If you stop drinking . . .')

are probably as hollow as his ('I would stop drinking if . . .') and the traditional threats are those of leaving or seeking a divorce. At the same time she relinquishes the enabling activity. Perhaps she perceives the negative effect it has on his drinking, or just recognises the futility of the exercise. To some extent she is withdrawing from the problem for her own sanity, adopting an attempted indifference in order to render herself immune to further hurt or loss of her own self-worth.

Self-worth relies considerably on how we are viewed by others. She may be satisfied in this to some extent by the obvious admiration of close friends and aquaintances who see how she is striving to cope and help her partner in any way possible, but the main source at first is the alcoholic partner, partly because of the innate closeness of the matrimonial bond, but also because of the increased isolation and inter-dependence bred by the disease. Once she withdraws her co-operation from him she is forced to look elsewhere. Where and how she looks will depend on circumstances and opportunities, or how best she can exploit her potential.

SEPARATION

She is forced to seek fulfilment elsewhere in order to establish again her sense of value. She may do this through work or social life, or both. She may seek new friends from whom she can seek image assurance. Some become workaholics, possibly branching out on new careers, but basically providing proving grounds of their own abilities and worth. Outside interests will grow so that she is no longer confined within the problem. Indeed she may see this as the reason for her actions. It is not unlike the geographic escape of the alcoholic, although less ill fated.

Technically the marriage is still intact, thus satisfying society and possibly adding to her self-image. But emotionally they have become separate. From his standpoint, both loneliness and a sense of desertion are paramount, and resentment is high. He can only interpret the entire development as one of failed love, which in his present state of critically low self-esteem seems justified and compounds the problem. The alcoholic may even try suicide, his anger being turned inwards. Her anger can rise to a similar uncontrolled pitch but is aimed at him, not herself. Subconsciously she may well wish him dead, the whole situation having now become too painful to accept. Fortunately for him, she is usually able to translate this as 'Get out of my life'. If not actually stated verbally, she will make this feeling apparent in a variety of ways, if necessary leaving him and establishing a new life elsewhere, evicting him from the matrimonial home, or seeking divorce. The threat has become a reality.

During this whole period, both the alcoholic and the partner have increasingly hidden their true feelings and built protective shells round themselves. This leads to the traditional emotional masks of blaming, excusing, denying, minimising and rationalising. This pattern becomes a way of life and presents the major obstacle to reforming the relationship should the drinking cease.

WHAT SHOULD BE DONE?

Many will resent the cold-blooded account given above, or even reject it completely. Obviously there are numerous variations, and not all motives are exactly the same. But I believe that the basic patterns of thinking are similar to those described above, and I think it is important to realise that the partner is affected very deeply by the situation, and that this cannot fail to induce some emotional sickness or even impaired mental and physical health.

For eventual recovery both of you have to understand the changes the disease has wrought in you both. Once the nature of the disease is recognised then support should be limited to sincere attempts to understand the problem and assurances of love. The alcoholic should know that his partner is there and shares his problem, but that she will not shelter him from those discomforts the disease brings, and why she will not. Although she will need to re-establish self-esteem even these endeavours can be underpinned with assurances of love; they need not be spiteful or revengeful. If understood, they can be used to strengthen the partner for potential reunion. But they need to be honestly embraced and explained, and the dangers of stifled feelings or perverted emotions recognised and corrected with honesty.

I believe that after reading the book and understanding the real nature of the disease much of the misunderstanding and distress can be avoided and be replaced by mutual commitment.

WHAT DO WE NEED FOR A GOOD RELATIONSHIP?

Passion is the colouring, the life, the excitement, the light of a relationship; it is not just sex. Most of us accept that a relationship relying on sexual attraction alone will not last, yet we do not always concede that the sexual attraction is not as ephemeral as implied, but is itself dependent on our spiritual communion. It is sad that in general the word 'love' serves only to conjure up in our minds some passionate relationship between a male and female, usually involving the sexual aspects of their individual charms. True, this is one of the greatest delights that nature can bestow on us and should be fundamental to the marriage bond, both as an initiator, and evidence of continuity. But the continuity of the sexual experience is not based on novelty or physical exploration, but the continued evolution of the relationship. The mind of another human being is unique and stands a lifetime's exploration.

TAKE YOUR CLOTHES OFF, I WANT TO TALK TO YOU!

If we wish to enjoy the physical delights of love, we first remove our clothes. This symbolises our abandonment and vulnerability, giving and taking as total people, sharing both mind and body. A real relationship demands the removal of any artificial clutter that inhibits the fusion of two minds, an emotional disrobing. Yet many of us contrive to avoid this through shame or fear. We never take off our disguises, our masks, our clutter. Because we dare not expose ourselves to the light of truth, we find ourselves, by habit, more comfortable in the mental clothes that conceal our feelings.

We are all prone to developing defences, and imagine them to be necessary for survival. We are told (wrongly) that this is what life is all about. The alcoholic is convinced that his defences must be inviolable, and strives, partially subconsciously, to achieve this.

WHAT SHALL I WEAR TODAY?

Happy physical nudity depends on self-esteem (comfortable in oneself) and trust ('I understand and respect you, and believe you will not take advantage of me, or deceive me'). In a healthy physical relationship the nudity is not confined to the bedroom, except for convenience, and is symptomatic of evolving and growing trust, and mutual self-esteem. So should it be with our feelings. People cannot survive in isolation, they need another mind with which to exchange feelings, test their validity and allow them to evolve. Without total emotional honesty such a vital exchange cannot occur. By the building of defences we insulate our minds from real life, forfeit our right to evolve and deny that right to others. Our responsibilities as human beings lie in offering ourselves up to relationships and thus allowing for the spiritual evolution that is man's destiny. We are offered this chance each day with every human being with whom we come into contact. Such honest sharing is the real basis of love in its widest sense. If we are fortunate we will encounter at least one other mind during our lifetime with whom we have the privilege of a total and honest sharing of life.

We have to *like* our partner, not just love him or her. This needs the free expression of our feelings, unhindered by masks or disguises, and honest confrontation and acceptance of our partners motives. Concern for each other's wellbeing is vital, as is a total commitment to the relationship. This means hard work and earnest endeavour. Only by the true sharing of minds can we increase our individual gifts. And only by sharing can we understand love.

Sir Henry Drummond in his book *The Greatest Thing in the World* lists the components of love as: patience, kindness, generosity, humility, courtesy, unselfishness, good temper, guilelessness and sincerity. The Bible (I Cor. 13xiii) says 'And now abideth faith, hope, love, these three; but the greatest of these is love'.

5 Defences

Although defences are universal and not the prerogative of the alcoholic, addict or partner, the magnitude of the alcoholic's problem necessitates building an unusually strong defence-system, and this constitutes a prominent and constant feature of the disease. Through repetition these patterns of behaviour become familiar, comfortable and the norm.

SOME EXAMPLES

No defence is so marked as that of 'denial'. The alcoholic may deny to others or to himself, the latter usually being far more effective and certainly the most dangerous. 'Of course I haven't had a drink' is far from convincing coming from he of the slurred speech and glassy eye, appropriately smothered in peppermint, toothpaste and after-shave! But 'Of course I haven't a drink problem' is probably aimed largely at himself in a desperate bid to avoid facing the inevitable. He has no intention of doing anything about the problem, so he has to deny its existence.

We will all deny that which we do not wish to know, hence our avowels of not being angry or hurt or frightened; very often it is our undue emphasis that proves the very truth we are trying to deny. This is known as 'compensation' or 'reaction formation'. Exaggerated statements of behaviour are used to deny feelings of an opposite tendency which are threatening but probably unconscious. I am not homosexual/racist/puritanical, for example. A man may have many girl friends to show he is not homosexual, or for that matter be a total abstainer to show that drink has no power over him. An unhappy friend of mine would ostentatiously sink a single and slow pint in the local bar every lunch-time, to conceal the fact that he was secretly drinking shorts throughout the day.

Denial will extend into many areas of the alcoholic's life, denial of where he has been, denial of how much he has drunk or spent, denial of having been drunk or guilty of unacceptable behaviour. Denial becomes a way of life, and comes more easily with practice.

Minimising is another characteristic of the alcoholic: 'It was not that bad' or 'It was not that much'. Minimising can often take the form of 'conning' or concealing. The alcoholic may remove the empties to 'con' his partner over the amount drunk, or conceal the supply to hide his need. But he is much more subtle in the way he will 'con' himself. He does not wish to know how much he has drunk or how much it has cost. When he counts his money at the end of the week, he will exaggerate every item of expenditure so that he can obtain a satisfactory (to himself) estimate of the residual amount spent on drink. The drink bought with the weekly shopping will receive the same treatment. I did this repeatedly.

Perhaps my personal greatest 'con' concerned praying. When particularly troubled by my drink problem I would invariably ask for help and guidance in my evening prayers, but if I prayed in the mornings I would not refer to drink. Yet I knew really that this was the most vital time. Why did I behave like this? Because I already knew that I would take a drink and my conscience would either not allow me to pray hypocritically, or it would make it exceedingly difficult to drink having prayed. So I only brought the problem up in the evening, presumably in the hope of forgiveness for the daily lapse. Yet I never fully admitted this to myself.

Another favourite deception of mine was to buy a bottle, not because I intended drinking, but 'just in case of an emergency', which I invariably drank, inventing the emergency if necessary. Similarly I would religiously count my money before leaving home, yet rarely admitted to myself that it was to check whether I had enough to pick up a bottle 'if required'. But I would panic if there were insufficient funds.

Concealing can also be more subtle and concern the effects of drink or the need for it: shopping in the area of the off-licence, running out of cigarettes just before opening time, collecting the newspapers just before noon on Sunday, a voluntary task carried out with enthusiasm. The offending bottle would be hidden about the person (I even chose my clothes with this in mind).

Such stories are monotonous and repeated with variations by every alcoholic; inevitably the lying, denying, minimising and concealing form stifling, rigid patterns that are difficult to break.

Devaluing is a further unhappy strategy of the alcoholic, shared with all those of low self-esteem. Alcoholics are very quick to condemn others as drinking too much, or having a problem, the accusations hopefully taking the spotlight off them, and making their own case less chronic. This is a form of 'projection'. In more desperate circumstances the accusation may bear no relation to drink, but be more in the nature of a general character assassination. 'If you think I'm lousy, look at *her* husband' The whole object is to make it seem that, taken on balance, you with drink, is better than others without. Here again, this inappropriate critical faculty can become incorporated into your life, operating regardless of need and clouding judgement. These unwarranted attacks on others are a form of displacement from one's own problems.

Introjection is another tactic used. You diminish your pain with reflected glory from images or things. The alcoholic is not only singularly dramatic in his life-style, but frequently self-dramatises. He casts himself in an Homeric role, pitting his wits against life and adversity. He alone can see clearly. He thus adds stature to his otherwise pathetic struggles and avoids the real pain. Admittedly, in some respects his life *is* a tragi-comedy, reminiscent of the best Shakespearian traditions! A recklessness with money is characteristic of the alcoholic, and quite often he is a great acquisitor. Many of those things he acquires are status symbols and reflect a need to enhance the external image to offset the deterioration within. Be especially wary of the known alcoholic who turns up looking excessively well-groomed. It is probably one of his worst days. 'But we all do that' you protest. Quite so. Nothing unique. Just more desperate and more marked.

Attempts to explain drinking, rather than deny it or face it, fall into three categories, excusing, blaming and rationalising, and by far the greater of these is rationalising. They all represent feeble attempts to justify. Whatever we do wrong we all have excuses and there are plenty of people or events to blame, but no-one has such a constant need to justify himself as the alcoholic who 'does something wrong' several times a day. His is a full-time task. The objects of blame include his work, wife, family, finances, friends, social life, health or things in general. It does not matter whether work went well or badly; it is an excuse for either drowning the sorrows or celebrating. And with a bit of luck his drinking will cause a further deterioration in all the items, thus calling for another round of drinks. He may not consciously appreciate this, indeed it is the last of his objectives, but unhappily this is the likely outcome and is self-perpetuating. Things are bad, have a drink, and things will get worse.

What he does not register in all this is that the drink is far more important than the so-called cause. He looks for the excuse or the person to blame, and when he finds a scapegoat he really believes it provides justification. And once the circuit is established, every failure is capable of being linked to another event, continually 'passing his own buck' as it were, and never facing the reality.

He is not owning his own feelings, but blaming events external to himself for controlling his feelings. In the case of people, he even attributes motives to them, he is judgemental. 'She wanted to make me angry, she made me angry, so I drank'. He cannot see that only the last is true. He can become quite paranoid, believing that events and people are actively conspiring against him. He is placing judgement on other peoples feelings which he has no right or reason to do.

Rationalisation is our biggest deceit, applying to ourselves as well as others, being unlimited in its application, and often by its very nature exceedingly difficult to fault or contradict. The higher the intelligence, the more devastating its effect. It is, in essence, a perversion of logic, skilled verbal juggling. To rationalise should imply 'bringing into conformity with reason' but a sinister alternative offered by the Oxford dictionary is 'find plausible or reasonable motives'. If we then look up 'plausible' we have (deceptively) 'seeming reasonable or probable, *apparently* honest, true'. Need we say more! We are using our intellectual powers to *apparently* justify an idea or action, to support an action which we may well *know* to be wrong. It is akin to the guilty having the right to be proven innocent if a legal loop-hole can be found. Truly the devil's advocate. It is fun to be able to argue convincingly on either side of a debate, so long as we do not fool ourselves.

But when we use rationalisation deliberately to deceive ourselves or others it is a very powerful and evil weapon. And more than any other of the defence mechanisms it is highly addictive, soon being applied in most aspects of our living. We cease to notice the extent to which we use it, and can convince ourselves that virtually any action can be justified. By the use of skilled rationalisation we can think or argue our way to any pre-conceived conclusion we may desire, we can modify our value systems to our own ends, justify any action we wish to take, modify morality according to circumstance, take no responsibility for our failures. It is the ultimate corruption of values, the antithesis of truth, honesty and integrity. The devil's gift to the alcoholic.

ATTACK YOUR DEFENCES

How do you do this? By being aware of your defences. By watching the way in which you instinctively defend some wrong, and questioning both your real motive and the real validity, if any, of your defence. Perhaps the question to ask yourself is would you have found another defence if that one had not been available?

I find that continued monitoring of my own motives reveals to me the state of my defences, and it becomes second-nature to recognise their artificiality. I find that dropping my defences gives me far greater freedom. I own my feelings again, and I like them. Dare I say it, I even like me! There is no surer way of encouraging defence in others than by defending oneself. One might see it as the 'disguise deterrent', compelled to escalate on both sides. So how about a gradual mutual disarmament? Honesty is contagious. Most people manage to remain reasonably human for much of the time. They will be glad to see you back, and will start talking to you again. Communication! Hello, world. It could be fun. I know it is.

6 The Problems of Withdrawal

THE ESSENTIAL BALANCE: HOMEOSTASIS

Consider your very being, your body, your life, your existence. The ultimate scientific analysis will allow us to perceive life as a highly organised system of mass and energy. This simplification does not denigrate life. A good analogy would be to state that a Leonardo da Vinci drawing viewed under a high power microscope would be revealed to us as no more than dots and space. So would a two year old's scribble. It is the intricacy of assembly that inspires awe, whether it be in response to life itself or Leonardo's crude imitation. This is why you, who are alive, differ from a stone, which is dead. We are told the difference is one of complexity and organisation, but I think to this we should add purpose. It also helps us understand our 'one-ness' with the universe and the astonishing inter-relationships, only very few of which we comprehend.

Considering the baffling complexity of the atom, a basic unit of all matter whether living or dead, and the giant step to the living cell we cannot help but be impressed by the miracle we call life. As Dr Lovelock points out in his book 'Gaia: A New Look at Life on Earth' life is instantly recognisable but almost impossible for us to define, except in terms of reduced entropy. This implies the use of energy to organise life at the expense of its surroundings, which are characterised by increasing disorder, or chaos. The whole concept would require an intricate system of balance in which no system could be seen in isolation.

To sustain life the body must maintain internal and external equilibrium, harmony in complexity. Constancy of temperature, acidity or alkalinity, heartbeat and breathing, the levels of essential fuels and regulating chemicals. And it must respond continuously to changes in the environment. Thus we begin to visualise the intricate molecular juggling required to sustain life. The majority of this control is carried out unconsciously by a vast electro-chemical complex continuously monitoring all external and internal changes that occur, and making the necessary adjustments. Homeostasis is the name given to this phenomenom in which the essential *status quo* is maintained against all change, whether internal or external. The endocrine (hormone) and nervous systems play a vital role.

HORMONES AND STRESS

The hormone adrenalin is familiar to the schoolchild as the Fright, Flight or Fight hormone, mobilising our body chemistry to meet emergencies. Adrenalin is produced by the adrenal medulla. A further response to stress is shown by the pituitary gland which produces adreno-corticotrophic hormone (ACTH) which in turn stimulates the adrenal cortex to produce cortisone, also combatting stress. But cortisone controls the initial production of ACTH, thus providing a self-regulating response known as a negative feedback system. Self-regulation by negative feedback systems is fundamental to communication and control in the body, and emphasises that no system can be adequately studied in isolation, each being dependent on another. We interfere with this fine balance at our peril.

Dr Hans Selye, the distinguished endocrinologist, implicates the overproduction of adrenal hormones in stress to a number of major diseases and visualises a breakdown in hormonal mechanisms as being the ultimate cause of death. A change in one hormone will be reflected by changes elsewhere in the endocrine system. Apart from specific functions they are largely interdependent and form networks of communication. The sex hormones may be the last to be established, adding the final flourish to the canvas, but by completing the picture they add far more than sex to the vision of the adolescent.

There is a close connection between the endocrine and nervous systems. Adrenalin is almost identical to the neuro-transmitter noradrenalin, produced at the ends of the sympathetic nerves, and both play a similar role in response to stress. We now acknowledge the roles of both neurotransmitters and endomorphins in behaviour and reaction to stress. Significantly both beta-endomorphin and ACTH spring from a common chemical precursor (pro-opiocortin), but whereas ACTH induces general hyperactivity and stimulates sexual behaviour, endomorphins act antagonistically, depressing these. A further example of interdependence and the essential balance. Professor Sandler and his colleagues at Queen Charlotte's Hospital, London, believe the body has its own 'panic' molecule, called tribulin. This is thought to equilibrate with the naturally occurring equivalent of valium in the body, thus maintaining an appropriate emotional balance.

The importance of maintaining equilibrium and the inter-dependence of bodily processes is increasingly demonstrated. Exciting work in the field of immunology suggests that the defending macrophages in the blood 'recognise' stress induced cortisol and function less efficiently against infection. Fortunately this adverse effect of stress can be counteracted by stimulating our endomorphin production through exercise. Increased endomor-phin production is thought to explain the 'jogger's high'. Does the body instruct us to pace up and down when agitated? Nalaxone, a synthetic antagonist to all opioids including endomorphins is said to attenuate the jogger's high, and even to interefere with our enjoyment of music.

The study of self-regulating systems of communication and control is cybernetics, and Lovelock concludes that the primary function of cybernetic systems is 'to steer an optimum course through changing conditions towards a predetermined goal'. Increasingly we are glimpsing something of the highly intricate cybernetic network controlling every aspect of our being from our build to our behaviour. Our responsibility lies in how we use this given framework. I believe it is not only ours to obey but ours to command by appropriate inter-reaction with our physical, emo-tional and spiritual environment. The mental or physical environ-ment we super-impose on the gene we inherit.

THE COST OF DOUBTING THE SYSTEM____

Incredibly, you decided that this intricate and elaborate system was inadequate for your particular needs. You invoked alcohol, or a drug, to manipulate the system. You not only meddled with this miraculous and highly sensitive mechanism, but you attempted to fool the body by using chemicals vaguely familiar to it, those that would directly or indirectly function as natural opiates. By doing so, you well and truly clobbered the system. Perhaps by now you can see why it would not work and could not work, and appreciate not only the damage you have done, but the extent of the repair work and the length of time required for recovery. The entire stress-response system has been thrown out of balance, and withdrawal of your anaesthetising crutch will have dramatic short- and long-term effects.

DRYING OUT OR DETOX____

Depending on the amount drunk and for how long, many of us will have experienced to some degree the dreaded effects of sudden withdrawal from our alcohol (or drug) supply. These can range from little more than discomfort and craving for a drink, to a range of symptoms such as tremors ('the shakes'), sweats and nausea, to quite violent and potentially dangerous symptoms such as black-outs; delirium tremens or convulsions. Any or all of these might well be accompanied by some degree of mental confusion, or a certain lack of ability to co-ordinate our thinking or speech exactly as we would wish. The slightest trauma will probably throw us. Altogether very unpleasant and under-estimated by many.

Not surprisingly, they manifest themselves somewhere between 12 and 72 hours after the last drink, probably peaking around 24-36 hours. From shortly after that last drink the blood alcohol level is falling and is soon insufficient to calm our shattered nervous system. The body is meanwhile fighting a desperate battle to restore equilibrium, generally coping with the most bizarre effects within

72 hours. It is remarkable that it survives at all.

On top of this there is the psychological dimension. Anticipation of withdrawal symptoms results in a degree of apprehension having its own nervous reaction, similar to the anticipation of the effects of the drink *immediately* on consuming liquor when a degree of calmness supervenes long before the alcohol has a chance to be absorbed. The body is very good at telling you what to expect, allowing you a 'coming shortly'. A strong overlay of panic might edge a situation of acute nervous tension into one inducing a convulsion. Quite a mild tranquiliser might have a valuable and immediate placebo effect.

What is actually happening? At its simplest, and bearing in mind all we have said, the brain has become devoid of defence against stress. It is naked and raw, and very vulnerable. A relatively normal stimulus will produce an outsize response. The man with a hangover is frequently portrayed creeping stealthily about, dramatically upset by the slightest noise: a revealing picture. I have certainly experienced the effects of a spontaneous 'crack' on the radio reverberating round my entire system. Every alarm responds! Seen like this, it is obvious that 'pull yourself together' or 'it can't be that bad' are inappropriate comments. It *is* that bad, and you cannot pull yourself together. You are suffering from a biochemical imbalance which only time can heal. Or, of course, a drink.

It is very important for those nearest to you, to appreciate the severity of the condition. The man or woman who succumbs to a quick drink during this period is not *just* showing a total lack of willpower, or satisfying a mere craving for a drink in the obvious sense. He or she, perhaps foolishly, is desperately attempting to remove unbearable symptoms which may be quite alarming, totally incapacitating, and even dangerous. The strain on the system is very real. Cardiac arrest is rare but not impossible.

Because of the psychological dimension it is *not* appropriate to persuade the drying-out alcoholic to 'get out and enjoy yourself' or 'come out and meet people – just because you're not drinking there is no need to become antisocial'. I have no doubt that such unsolicited advice is well intended. The other person cannot understand how you feel, and 'getting back into life' or 'rejoining the human race' appear as positive steps to recovery. So they are, but not immediately. It is a hard thing to say, but premature re-entry is a sure way to taking just a couple of drinks to smooth the entry.

A convulsion can be a very frightening experience for all concerned. It is indicative of a fairly advanced stage of chronic alcoholism. It is for these reasons that detoxification should be carried out under medical supervision, and some form of sedative used. A decreasing dose of librium, for example, can be given over a period of days, heart-rate and blood-pressure being monitored. In less severe cases, self-medication with prescribed drugs will be effective. Having said that, it cannot be over-emphasised that for ultimate recovery from alcoholism, any mood-altering chemical must be avoided in the long term. They could become a replacement psychological crutch, and they inhibit the renewal of the natural body defences essential to ultimate well-being.

The whole emphasis of the programme of recovery we are covering is one of learning to face the world again with total honesty and pride. No artificial defences can be used. Indeed, no defences of any kind – we must be naked and unashamed from a mental, emotional and spiritual standpoint.

THE LONGER-TERM SYMPTOMS

The first two years are the worst. This is overstated perhaps, but it is better to be forewarned. The remarkable resilience of the body is reflected in its apparent physical recovery in a matter of days or weeks, the emphasis being on 'apparent'. No shakes, sweats or nausea, but beneath the surface the chemical damage remains, and is unlikely to recover for from 6 months (heroin) to 2 years (alcohol, tranquilisers). This does not imply that you will be a nervous wreck-craving for a drink or a drug all this time, but this may still happen.

It is very important that you understand that it is very unlikely that you will feel consistently well during this period, and that you accept the explanation offered. The symptoms may include emotional

A–G

states such as anxiety, panic, depression, irritability, vagueness and mental confusion. The physical symptoms may include muscular aches and pains, digestive upsets, lowered resistance to infection, even palpitations or 'missed beats'.

These symptoms can be severe and worrying. As they are considerably less dramatic than those experienced immediately following removal of alcohol or a drug, they may not be readily associated with this removal. They can become a source of further anxiety, legitimate concern and eventually resentment: the potentially destructive 'it's not fair' syndrome. 'I felt better when I was drinking' is a familiar, almost certainly inaccurate, but understandable complaint.

What has to be appreciated is that in exactly the same way that you knew during the initial acute withdrawal symptoms that alcohol or a drug would banish the discomfort, so too will it be tempting now, consciously or subconsciously, to escape from this extended discomfort.

The real hazards are the emotional troughs, or periods of confusion, characterised by indecision, irritability, uncertainty. You may even become accident prone. It is all too easy to panic at such times, literally to doubt your sanity, and be tempted to grab the most effective and rapid antidote you know. These periods played a major role in many of my own failures to maintain sobriety, and I know how compelling the feelings can be. I cannot over-emphasise the danger of this time. Deep conditioning tells you that 'instant wellbeing' is only an off-licence away, but one medicinal drink soon becomes a protracted therapy.

It is important to know that the symptoms are those of recovery rather than disease, and to endure them in the knowledge that they can only become less with time. Understanding is the key to acceptance. Just remember that it will be easy, without conscious thought, to slip back into a familiar cycle of poor health and negative attitudes and to find the old rationalisations or excuses for that drink or drug. Often it is the bizarre and unrelated nature of the symptoms that provides conclusive evidence for there being no real organic basis. Bear in mind, however, that you *have* ill-treated every part of your body for some time, and that as well as this you are subject to life's normal vicissitudes.

It will do no harm to consult your doctor should especially uncomfortable symptoms persist. But do explain to him exactly what the situation is. You will find that most doctors (indeed, most people) will be delighted and sympathetic and more than ready to encourage and help wherever they can. Unfortunately, the standard treatment for your complaint is tranquillisers and you must resist these as strongly as you would a drink. Explain to your doctor that all mood-altering chemicals are out.

As regards emotional demands, treat yourself kindly. It will make a change and be appreciated by your long-suffering mind and body. Alcoholics Anonymous stress that their programme is 'selfish'. For good reason. At this time the most important gift you can give to yourself or others is sobriety, and that must have priority over all other matters. There is little point in rushing back to work, for example, if you are not yet ready to cope with the pressures. There is little point in forcing yourself to be sociable if you are going to feel excessively uncomfortable. You are not running or hiding. You had cause before, but not now. Edge slowly back into the mainstream. Remember, you have only your sobriety to prove – give the rest time and it will surely follow. Most of all remember how disastrous your previous 'proving' became. Whilst in treatment I was offered the following very sane choice. 'Either accept that you are not perfect, or start getting perfect.' An obvious choice that tells us much about our unrealistic perfectionism!

7 A Power Outside Ourselves

It is strange that many people are reluctant to accept that some source of special power is available to us which is not confined specifically to ourselves, a power which is shared and universal. Perhaps it is our ultimate egocentricity that denies this: we maintain that we not only have complete control over ourselves, are totally self-sufficient and autonomous, but expect to manipulate the external world to meet our own ends. Through arrogance we deny anything outside our intellects or imaginations and believe that nothing exists unless we can prove it or fully comprehend it.

Centuries ago, it would have been quite impossible to tell someone about magnetism and electricity. Not only would the effects appear impossible or magical, but the background knowledge necessary to explain these phenomena would not have been available, or within the experience of the listener. He would have to have had enormous faith in us to accept what we said as true, and most people would doubt his sanity for so doing. It was Bergson, who drew the analogy of trying to explain the world as we know it to the most intelligent earthworm in the world. No matter how sophisticated its brain, the sheer limitations of its sensitivity to temperature, touch and vibrations would preclude any hope of understanding. So why do we assume that our accepted five senses will interpret everything in our world for us? Biologically speaking, they enable our survival, no more; that is their purpose.

A complex organisation of matter and energy has produced what we know as life, and we are but a part of it. Undoubtedly our beings are subjected to many forces, many influences of which we have very little understanding, but when we consider our bodies as micro-units in some enormous power structure our credulity in the unknown should not be over-stretched. The phrase 'the unknown' is not mystical. It just means that we do not know. And 'I don't know' is not an admission of failure, or denial of that which we do not know, but a simple statement of fact regarding our natural limitations. When we consider the mind-boggling nature of the universe, and how totally incomprehensible and miraculous it is to us, how can it detract in any way from our significance, our own personal miracle, to accept that we are but a part of it? In that sense, the power of which we speak is also universal, and we have a right to a share in it. It is there, if we care to use it. It is outside us and inside us. Too frequently we choose to ignore it.

What we call our material or concrete world may well be just a construction of reality enabling us to live, survive, and attend to our needs. The nature of life itself can only be experienced, not defined. Biologically we have to define a living entity as opposed to a dead one, by describing its attributes – feeding, moving, reproducing, sensing and so on. Even so, we know what life is. If we close our eyes and shut out all extraneous sounds and even mental imagery, it is possible with great effort and practice to feel the surge of life of which we are part. This is the 'intuition of reality' described by Wilson Carr, and may be more real than the so-called reality of everyday necessity. If you open your eyes again, the sense of the continuous flow of life is fragmented, and we perceive the world like the successive frozen frames of a video or film.

These approaches help to convince us that a limited concept of reality might be false. That which we feel may be much closer to reality than that which we sense. So we have to trust what we feel.

There is nothing new in this idea. Long before Christ, the Stoics saw 'God' as an all-pervading force, 'related to the world, as the soul is related to the body'. The general concept that God can be identified with all that exists is known as Pantheism and has been followed since early Greek days, and in recent times by Spinoza and Butler. Butler believed in creative evolution and saw the ultimate goal as spiritual perfection, a wholeness of mind and body. In all these philosophies it is necessary to accept that a collective power exists which is much greater than the individual.

WHAT SHALL WE CALL IT?

We could, of course, try to put a name to this universal power or quality. We never seem to be happy unless we can name something or label it. How about 'God'?

Man is a great model maker; he is always constructing working models for various aspects of life. He has to give names to the various components so he can refer to them as necessary and draw on them to construct new models. An atom is really mass and energy, and even mass and energy are no more than useful labels for unimaginable concepts. I said unimaginable concepts and this is an accurate description for the reality is outside the reach of our imaginations. The words and explanations allow us to 'visualise' and we do this by relating all concepts to things that are within the light of our personal experience. But the very real hazard is that we limit ourselves by using these labels, assuming them, falsely, always to define specific and concrete realities.

Nowhere is this seen more dramatically than in our use of the word 'God'. Many atheists who claim not to believe in God are in fact only doubting the existence of the popular image of God. In its extreme form this takes the form of an old gentleman with a questionable disposition, sitting on a cloud, exhibiting wild swings between benevolence and fury. They have attached a concrete image to a label chosen originally to describe something outside our comprehension. Most denials of God stem not from a disbelief in the powers attributed to Him but from the limitations of the man-made model.

It is strange that we accept that faith is a 'spiritual apprehension of divine truth apart from proof', and yet try to pin-down or limit the central figure! Especially when most would accept that the 'Spirit of God' is both universal and limitless.

It is for this very reason that Alcoholics Anonymous uses the phrase 'God as we understand Him' instead of just 'God'. This is not as some assume as a 'loophole' for doubters, but in acknowledgement of the difficulty of a universally satisfying definition. The concept of 'God' may mean many different things to as many people, yet it usually carries an assurance of power, strength, love, right and goodness. It represents all we hope for, and strive for, and is the stimulus for both.

Life has to be defined by its attributes, and so does love, but we have all experienced them. Why then do we hesitate to accept God? For many faith is only experienced when there is a need, and when all other help fails. That being so, it should be remarkably easy for the alcoholic to find.

WHY IS IT SO IMPORTANT TO US?

The need for faith in a higher power is not confined to the alcoholic. It is a general need without which our lives can be very sterile. There are those who feel that the continuing search for a spiritual basis to life is no more than wishful thinking. But nature never invents appetites without reason; we need to be reminded about hunger, thirst, sleep or sex, those drives that ensure survival of the species. They can be satisfied, and they *need* to be satisfied.

The spiritual drive has preoccupied Man for as long as life has been recorded, is innate, and is as real and vital to survival as other needs. There is ample testimony as to its reality in most fields of human endeavour or triumph over adversity, nationally or individually. In view of such evidence, so well chronicled, it is incredible that we should doubt it. Yet we do, because we cannot hold it in our hands, or look at it under a microscope. We can only feel it, yet we still fail to trust those feelings.

Many alcoholics undergoing therapy find the insistence on belief in a higher power a little worrying, as if a magic ingredient has been introduced to wash clean their souls. 'I knew there was a catch' or 'More religious rubbish' are quite usual reactions. This is to misunderstand. Organised religion is only one of man's efforts to deal with the spiritual side of life. A brave one, and a good one, but not necessarily the only one.

It has been said, very wisely, that it is easier to define God by what he is not, rather than what he is and the word 'he' can be very offputting for many. All the alcoholic needs to acknowledge initially is that some spiritual power exists in which he has a right to claim a share. There is no need to define or restrict the nature of that power. To know it is sufficient. It may help to relate it to the rest of one's experience. Some see God in nature, or as the collective mind of mankind; some see it more finitely as the trust, thought and will of their AA group. By far the majority start from 'next to nothing' and finish with 'God as I understand him'. You need to be able to call on this tremendous power which is at once both inside you in its availability, and outside you in that it transcends your personal will. Perhaps we can see it as a power of goodness, a power of truth, a power of love, an untarnished positive quality.

Given such free-ranging choice for your higher power, what reason have you for doubting its validity? And should you seriously doubt the need for such belief, I ask you to look at the evidence set by those who have succeeded in recovering from alcoholism. It is the keystone of the AA programme, and there can be no doubt it has brought sobriety to thousands who previously had no hope. It is summarised in their second and third steps:

'Came to believe that a Power greater than ourselves could restore us to sanity.'
'Made a decision to turn our will and our lives over to the care of God as we understood him.'

LOOK AT IT ANOTHER WAY, YOU'RE A HELL OF A LOUSY DRIVER

It is quite possible that you have decided to reject any possibility of some nebulous higher power playing a part in your life, certainly not one that transcends your will. You find it outrageous; how can you build self-esteem by admitting that you need outside help? Should you do this, then your confusion is even greater than I anticipated, for I have tried to explain that it is not simply outside help: you may well be appealing to that which is best inside you, that part you have been ignoring, or has become hidden by drink, that part of you which you wish to find again.

When you talk about your will, you really mean 'self-will', the part of you which is largely responsible for getting you into the position you are presently occupying. And is certainly responsible for keeping you there. It is the great I of the immediate needs. Any claim to independence is quite derisory when you consider how your life has been dominated by the bottle, and tied irrevocably to drink. We are all, to some extent, a synthesis of good and bad qualities, positive and negative values, but drink leaves no room for the former whereas a higher power demands the room occupied by the latter.

It is pathetically true that the alcoholic likes to feel in control, to be in 'the drivers seat'. Pathetic in the sense that it is patently obvious to others that he has lost all semblance of control ages ago, and if he's driving its a hell of a rotten journey. The alcoholic needs to concede that he cannot run his life on his own. If you are an alcoholic you have already admitted that you are powerless over alcohol and that your life has become unmanageable. You have proven your need for more than just yourself, your need for a faith. It is there for the asking, and only in seeking it, finding it, recognising it and sharing it will you find real freedom and 'independence'.

I DO BELIEVE BUT MY LIFE IS STILL A MESS___

Looking back on what I have written, I am aware that I have largely excluded from my discussion those alcoholics who do believe in 'God' in the orthodox sense, or those whose lives already include a religious component. This can cause its own special type of pain, the alcoholics' behaviour conflicting openly with all they profess to believe. This very conflict in turn becomes a cause for further drinking. But neither issue is being fully faced.

They often feel that their God has deserted them, or they feel angry with God for allowing them to destroy themselves. It is curious that they do not see that it is they who have deserted God, not vice versa. They might protest that they have constantly entreated the help of God, but to no avail. But they will also know that they have not truly listened. Their plea for help has almost certainly been conditional, to enable their will to proceed, not his will. And 'God' will set a very good example by refusing to be cast in the role of enabler! Their pre-occupation with the drink problem will leave no real space for God, and their distorted values will rarely recognise 'God'. Prayer may be heavy in quantity but singularly lacking in quality.

My own faith, for example, includes Christ as a man who lived and told us so much of 'God as we understand him'; whose spirit still prevails and to whom I can pray. I accept it to be a very imperfect faith, but one that sustains me and gives meaning to my life. I pray to understand more.

But I know that I have often been guilty of trying to deceive my 'God', even in prayer. I am grateful that he was not susceptible! And my punishment continued, not I think, by 'God', but by myself. How else could I learn? I also know that I was offered many signs and opportunities but I would ignore them, even though recognising them, and make the wrong choice. Such is the power of the addiction. Such is the self-will it nurtures. I was never angry with 'God'. How could I be, when I knew that all I hated of myself was that which was 'not God'. I knew my faith became shallow when obsessed with drink, for the faith had little room in which to flow, but I knew equally that I would never be deserted, and that in need, some answer would come from my prayer. Yet I continued my self-destruction for many years. I lived in a cage entirely of my own making. I could not have grasped freedom had it been offered, so restricted and confined were my horizons. Only when it became apparent that the bars were illusory could I start to recover.

It was like being in a tiny and rather dingy room. Outside the storm clouds let all hell loose. I got used to my own four walls and restricted vision and even congratulated myself on my survival. Suddenly the rain stopped, out came the sun, and I saw clearly, seemingly for the first time. New perspectives, infinite possibilities. That was recovery.

I was reluctant to include anything about my own faith, but hope perhaps it will do something to help those of a similar disposition to me. I can also say that, in recovery, my faith found space to breath again, and was a vital part of that recovery.

HOW DO WE FIND IT?

Well, you could try slowing down, and giving it time to climb aboard. However you should choose to envisage this special power, it is first necessary to grasp that it is there all the time, always has been and always will be. All you have to do is learn to recognise it. And recognition comes from familiarity. And familiarity, of course, stems from usage. Just imagine that you have bought some intricate new bit of gadgetry, indispensible in your home/office/garage/kitchen/workshop. It is likely you will spend many happy hours playing with it to be sure you know how it works and exactly when and where it will come in useful. Well, here you have the most vital tool, totally indispensible to your entire existence, handed to you on the proverbial plate. Does it not seem obvious to hold it, to check what it has to offer, or exactly how you would use it? As with the gadget, if you are not familiar with it then, when the opportunity to use it presents itself, either you cannot find it or you do not know how to use it. I am a keen photographer, and I like to tell people that my camera is like another eye, or even a hand, but certainly a part of me which I use instinctively. That is how this higher power must become: instinctive, part of you.

Of course, if you are really set on *not* finding it, there are two sure ways to guarantee that any search is abortive. You can avert your eyes and look continually inwards, or you can just make sure that all your senses are otherwise engaged on the trivia of life and thus immune to any signals. Both of these ploys are second nature to the alcoholic. It is obvious therefore that first you have partly to break through your alcoholic way of thinking just in order to create enough room for an initial foothold and give your spirit room to breathe.

WHAT ABOUT PRIDE?

Maybe your pride requires an overhaul, or preferably radical surgery and rebuilding. A chink in your false pride would not come amiss at this stage and might well make just the sort of space your mind and spirit require. Of course, you might well be exclaiming 'What pride?' and with some justification, should you be in the phase of shattered self-esteem or downright self-pity. But in general, even if you are approaching rock bottom, the odds are that your false pride will be alive and well.

Pride is an ambiguous word, occasionally used as a synonym of self-esteem, yet also included in the list of deadly sins, and encompassing vanity, egotism, arrogance and many other unattractive qualities. Properly used pride should denote an accurate evaluation of self-worth, and be the means of maintaining the standards related to, or expected from such an evaluation. Unfortunately we are not very good at pricing ourselves, and pride is subject to inflation in uncertain times. And here enters false pride, totally unambiguous and unmistakable, and leading to the 'Be your own God' syndrome.

Narcissistic, self-opinionated and harsh in its judgement of others, the aim of false pride is primarily to compete, and to put itself in a better light at the expense of others. But let us face it, when your entire life is in fragments, you have to salvage any debris to build a defence. Its ploys are many. You might put undue value on such trivial assets as you have, or you may just replace nasty names with nice ones, consciously or otherwise. Arrogance may travel in the guise of self-assertion, obstinacy may be seen as a strong-will, rationalising as wisdom, or the whole chaos of ones life attributed to being experienced or worldly. And all the time that you are plummeting downhill, you will, no doubt, pride yourself on your refusal to be beaten. The judgement aspect is not very appealing either, taking the form of slander or general character assassinations.

IT'S TOUGH BEING PERFECT IN AN IMPERFECT WORLD

False pride is closely allied to perfectionism hence the anomolous situation of the alcoholic whose life is totally disorganised yet who claims to be a perfectionist. Perfectionism should imply a striving to be perfect which in itself is highly laudable. But usually it reflects total intolerance, both of oneself and others. Standards are impossibly high and cannot be met. This makes the alcoholic dissatisfied and frustrated with himself and hyper-critical of others and of the world in general (thus, of course, presenting endless alibis for drowning his discontent in drink). Excess perfectionism is the 'Be your own God' syndrome: 'I am in charge, I am the driver, I am God and I expect my world to be perfect'.

Being God does impose a tremendous and needless strain. Imagine you are set a task. You have to do it perfectly, so you toil away repeating, perfecting, even starting again, showing it to no-one until it *is* perfect. No advice, no help. If you showed it to others before it was perfect, they would detect your weaknesses. Anyway there is no point in asking advice: you would not listen to it for you are already perfect. Carried to its extreme, this behaviour leads to the famous chronic non-finishing of the alcoholic, for nothing will ever be perfect.

Hyper-sensitive, hyper-critical, you name it, we have got it. We do in fact make lousy Gods, but fortunately for us, the real thing is compassionate and tolerant. And whilst we are standing in for 'God as we understand him' what need do we see for standing down and letting in the real 'God'.

LETTING GO

Think back to the last time you felt really ill. You had numerous responsibilities, lots of things needing your attention, and un-finished tasks and urgent demands surrounded you. But suddenly you felt so ill and incapable of coping that you admitted to your illness and took to your bed. You were probably well looked after; someone ministered to your needs and took care of your world for you. It survived and so did you. It was a really comfortable and relaxed feeling, because you had handed over to someone else.

Well, if you are an advanced alcoholic, you are very sick. You cannot cope. You have not done so in the past and you will not do so in the future. Why not accept that you do not have to be God any more. Just relax. What better time to hand over to that higher power than now. There is an old saying that 'God loves alcoholics' although I think it should read 'God *must* love alcoholics' considering how they survive in spite of their tenuous hold on life.

Sometimes I like to think that the whole disaster of the alcoholic springs from his conflict with spiritual power. This is defied from square one. Life canot be made whole without admitting to this power. The handing over to a spiritual power does not so much reflect a sudden and dramatic change, as an eventual admission that it is real and needed. The best type of defeat. Maybe that is why 'God' has a soft spot for alcoholics. He knows, and is waiting.

Bill D, the third member of the first AA group summed up the view of many future members: 'I came into AA solely for the purpose of sobriety, but it has been through AA that I have found God'. And he adds '. . . that is about the most wonderful thing a person can do'.

But it is vitally important to stress that we are talking of God as we individually understand that term. Regardless of individual beliefs we are talking about the recognition of a spiritual power which exists both inside and outside ourselves, a power vastly greater than any power we can claim as solely our own. It is only by handing over to that power that we can truly relax and find total freedom. We gain immeasurably by doing so, and sacrifice nothing save our faults.

WHAT ABOUT THE PAST?

In moments of despair, and there are far too many such moments, the alcoholic is wont to talk of the 'wasted years'. This can constitute a real hazard to recovery. 'What is the point in stopping now; it is too late', people say. This is not true. First of all, remember that this is only felt forcibly either before recovery or very early in recovery when the sheer delight of living has not been re-established.

Anger turned inwards is self-hate, and self-hate is directly connected with depression and even the suicide impulse. When the strangling fog of self-hate lifts an entirely new view is seen, and it is beautiful indeed. The content of the new view is so different from that which you perceived before, that only *then* can you see how jaundiced was your past view, and how incorrect your analysis. You had forgotten what real living was about.

I know that this may sound unlikely, or even sanctimonious, if you have been deeply disturbed by the extent of your loss. But I hope that at this stage you will accept the possibility of a new view and have trust. I have experienced it personally and witnessed it in countless others. They have found real happiness after much, if not all, seemed lost. Even the apparently lost may often quite miraculously be restored if the will, patience and faith are there.

The following exercise may seem curious, but try writing down what you have gained from drinking. Initially you will think of nothing, but think harder, and take your time. In the early days, before drink entirely dominated your life, many material benefits may have accrued. Think about alcoholics you have known or those you have heard about. Many were almost certainly highly successful before the one blemish of alcohol intruded into their lives. The creative worlds of literature, arts and science are far from free of alcoholism, and it is directly linked to ambition and drive in commerce and industry. Unfortunately it is rarely seen that this personality can still operate in the absence of alcohol, and eventually far more effectively. A good friend of mine who was a Fleet Street reporter could not believe that he would write even more fluently and imaginatively after recovery, yet he did so. He had an actual fear of sobriety, and the effect it would have on his life!

Perhaps it is right to stress here that this is a very real fear for many alcoholics: that their 'personalities' will suffer in sobriety, and that drink is essential to their self-expression. This is one of the great delusions, and is repeatedly shown to be untrue. It may take a little while for the natural confidence to be rebuilt, but it will happen and the individual will be far more intact and real than before. It is incredible that sobriety should pose more of a threat to the alcoholic than insobriety. The greatest self-deceit of them all.

Keep working on the positives gained from drinking. You will almost certainly have experienced many things that would not have come your way in sobriety, some good, some bloody awful. But experiences, nevertheless, and all experience forms some basis for learning.

Most of all you have pushed life to its limits, putting incredible strains on yourself and on others. The remarkable thing may be not what you have destroyed but what has *not* been destroyed. This will allow unsuspected strengths and values to emerge. The real significance of love, or of courage, will become more apparent. In many cases these would not have been so tested.

Only because of drink can you now see that you are truly not an island, that you cannot exist in isolation, and that you must evolve and change. You need other people, and need to have trust. You need continually to take stock of your values. Now once again remember that this need is not unique to alcoholism. It is within us all. But there are those whose lives are so unruffled they may never recognise this need.

If drink has achieved only this, it may have been necessary. It has forced you to start that long journey of self-understanding essential to life, the most important journey any of us can make. Your recovery is a tremendously exciting and revitalising revelation, leading to a life of continual re-assessment and self-examination, coupled with a real understanding and appreciation of others, and new born happiness.

In your case, it may be only through drink that you can come to recognise the spiritual power which gives meaning to your life. Others may have found it through patient search, or more often intuitively through other disasters or adversity. This will be your biggest gain from alcoholism and could well justify the whole exercise. Perhaps the first 'justification' over drinking that is actually justified!

WHY IS IT TAKING SO LONG?_____

Watch it! You are looking for the quick reward! A typical alcoholic approach. I have already emphasised the need to recognise and familiarise. There is a tendency to wait for the proverbial thunderbolt or supernatural vision, but such experiences are rarely documented and may be suspect. I believe that, with the exception of a fortunate few, the acceptance of a spiritual truth is a very gradual process. The more the power is used, the more it is recognised, and the more familiar it becomes the more it will be relied upon. It has to be nurtured and given serenity in which to grow. It needs constant communion, which some will see as prayer.

However you visualise it, however you best make contact with it, you will find that handing over to this higher power eventually brings you serenity, freedom, and oneness with the universe. It will be your strength and your guide.

I like the saying that you can have both humility and intellect, providing humility comes first.

HOW DO I EXERCISE THE POWER?_____

Our communion may take many different forms, but this spiritual power, which we all share, should take the role of a real friend who is always with you, with whom you can share problems and seek advice. You need never be alone, and will have a special quiet strength. It should become part of you, never more so than at the start and finish of each day.

Personally, and according to my understanding, I like to start the day by saying 'Thank you for the gift of this day, help me use it well'. This dispels any tendency to depression, fear or resentments, and sets my mind serenely and positively for the day ahead. Equally, at night, one can think or pray with gratitude for the happenings of the day, or for help in facing those problems to be faced. The 'handing-over' process is very evident here, usually bringing contented sleep.

But, like all exercise, it should be regular and not excessive.

A-H

Quality not quantity is what counts. It is a way of life, not just an occasional urgent request, not if it is to be fully realised.

As the saying goes, 'Go for it! You deserve it and can get it'.

And do not forget that this exciting exploration of yourself, others and life itself is a journey that never finishes. Each day is a new one with new experiences and fresh adventures, not to mention challenges. And it is made all the more exciting and easier if you take your friend with you through every step. You may falter, but you need never face total defeat again.

That goes for your whole programme of recovery. Of course there will be set-backs, but these can be seen as warnings or pointers; they are necessary. You have also rejoined the human race and have to take the rough with the smooth. The world is not perfect, and neither are you. Use yourself well, and allow others to do the same and to share the world with you. There is space for all.

8 Putting the Past Behind You

You know where you are going now. You have been given most of the directions and a not inconsiderable amount of equipment to help you stay on the path. You became sick through no real fault of your own – you did not knowingly create the damage – and you have seen how you were very reasonably unable to cope with the ensuing emotional chaos. You have also seen how you must reestablish your values, honesty and self-respect. You need to reintroduce purpose and direction into your life, in mind and spirit, and to see yourself in relationship not only to others but to life itself. Responsibility for your past has been largely removed and responsibility for your future restored. It is a new day with new hope and it is all very exciting. So what is holding you back, why the hesitation?

MISLAID ITEMS

There are probably quite a number of these in your drinking past; possibly a job, a home, or an entire family, none of which are easily replaceable. Without any one of them, or a host of minor losses, you find it difficult to plan ahead with any enthusiasm.

But I never cease to be astounded by the recuperative powers of the recovered alcoholic. Totally unexpected events can miraculously transform their lives from the despairing negative to the rewarding positive. It is quite extraordinary too how they can re-channel into exciting productivity that enormous amount of energy once dissipated in the effort of combining a drink problem with survival.

I have to entreat you to take one day at a time and to let go of past and problems, seeing today as 'the first day of the rest of your life'. Platitudes, yes, because they are true.

Immediate gratification is the usual demand of the alcoholic, and now is no exception. The rewards *will* come but they will take a variety of forms, some of which will barely have featured in your past and cannot be readily envisaged at the moment. They will come to you; you do not have to go out and grab them, and some you will recognise like long-lost friends, for that is what they are. Meanwhile you are working to restore the *quality* of your life. If you allow yourself to be overwhelmed by your losses, whether they involve your last £5 note or your home, then you will have neither the space nor the energy to strive for that quality. Grieve unduly for the past and you are likely to lose your future. Instead think of all the bloody awful things you have managed to lose.

GRIEF HURTS

Sad, yet good! Grief over a loss is a very real and honest feeling, and should be treated as such. Recognise the loss, own it and express it appropriately, and do not allow it to become destructive.

If a cat loses a leg, it does not ignore the fact or pretend it never happened. It accepts the loss and adapts its life accordingly. Otherwise it would undoubtedly fall over and most likely become a neurotic and antisocial cat. Failure to recognise a loss on your part will lead to parallel situations, where the perversion of your frustrated grief will lead into destructive negative feelings of envy or resentment, anger or guilt – and 'falling over'!

Once you have done this, let go of the loss and the grief. There should be no perpetual emotional shrine as this leaves no room for the growth of other emotions and they will surely wither. We have all seen those who lead a life devoted to grief for a lost relative or lover.

Adaptation to grief implies that we acknowledge the loss and re-make our lives in the light of this loss, not the darkness. It can be tough, but it is real and important, and we know we most admire those who accomplish it. Your life has to be planned taking account of the loss and you will need all your emotional energy to do this. Whatever your loss, it will not be unique. It is not just alcoholism which causes loss. Others sustain it by a death or the toss of a business coin. On the other hand, if there is any practical way of remedying the loss then go for it. You have never been in a better position than you are now to reverse the tide of affairs that has overtaken you.

The recovering alcoholic, often short of immediate practical involvement, called living by the rest of the world, has a great facility for projection. This is speculation about, or anticipation of, what might happen, forgetting the 'might not'. You *expect* to lose your job, the mortgage company *suggests* foreclosing, or your family have left home and you are *threatened* with divorce. But considering how alien you have found the world, it is amazing how co-operative it can become when it detects a glimmer of sanity on your part. But remember that it, or them, is still suffering some degree of shock.

And you have to accept that the seemingly inevitable will certainly pass beyond any doubt, should you continue to drink, or revert to drinking in one of your emotional troughs.

I FEEL SO ASHAMED

At this moment you may well feel that your self-esteem has gone forever, possibly with your partner or home. But this is not so, you just have to find it again, and find it you must, for without it your journey is fruitless, (and certainly not drinkless).

You may be protesting that you still have your pride, and that you are not beaten yet, but all that is very defensive and is bound up with a considerable amount of alcoholic arrogance and obstinacy. It is a long way from the serene acceptance of self, which is a balanced and entirely appropriate self-assuredness, leading to stable integration with the environment.

Most of us without any conscious effort maintain a relatively stable core of self-awareness, an unconscious balance sheet revealing our approximate worth, both debits and credits being shown. This is an honest self-assessment. But valuation has to be relative, there being no absolute standard, only a theoretical Christ-like ideal, which cannot help but reduce us all to the level of sinners, albeit forgivable ones. When we describe ourselves as being honest, it is relative to the honesty of others and is unlikely to constitute total honesty. Thus we tend to value ourselves relative to society.

The self-image is also promoted by external attributes such as job status, social class, particular achievements, or even material acquisitions such as home, car or clothes. The need to marry the 'right type' reflects in part the desire to perpetuate an image, or improve on it, and even the physical attributes of a partner can do this. Providing these externals are deserved they rightly contribute to self-esteem, but as we noted in Chapter 5 they may be forming part of a defence-system designed to bolster the flagging self-image. There are other defences, as discussed in Chapter 5.

The exaggerated perfectionism of the alcoholic may also still be causing problems. Remember that you are not God and cannot manipulate the world, otherwise you will again be in that self-perpetuating well of guilt and resentment.

TELL ME YOU LOVE ME BUT DON'T EXPECT ME TO BELIEVE IT!

If your self-esteem is low you may even hate yourself, so it is hardly surprising that the ex-alcoholic finds it difficult to accept love. Why should other people love him if he does not yet love himself? But since his self-esteem is usually based on the accolades accorded by others, he is paradoxically compelled repeatedly to seek confirmation of that which he doubts or knows not to be true.

There is nothing more depressing, and frustrating, for the partner than these constant requests for reaffirmation of love, the more so as they are never accepted. They are repeatedly rejected, only to be requested yet again, and there will be many occasions when the partner is equally unsure about the answer! This same insecurity is also reflected in his jealousy of potential rivals who to him appear better equipped in every respect. They all have looks, charm, wealth and intelligence, and are consistently sexually potent to boot. Very threatening. He fails to see that the greatest assets of these would-be lovers are firstly himself, with his self-denigration, and secondly their ability to remain sober and exercise their various talents to full advantage.

The ex-alcoholic is also characterised by the rejection of all gifts, an unbecoming quality shared with all those who feel unworthy. By gifts I mean anything from recognition of personal success, to compliments, to birthday or Christmas presents ('Wrong size/colour/shape; I'll change it' or 'Have it back, more use to you than me'). In fact, the extreme of these is simply refusing to be happy, as happiness is one of the greatest gifts of all. This fault-finding can become a permanent preoccupation and is very tiresome – so much so that the giver eventually sees little point in giving and the gifts are withheld. This provides the ex-alcoholic with the proof that he is unloved and reinforces the original self-hate. And throughout this emotional chaos his own 'infallible' instant reward of the demon drink or drug is available as consolation, as undemanding and unsharing as masturbation. A reward with an inbuilt guarantee of failure, because it is based on the inability to relate to others.

I KNEW IT WOULD'T WORK

Perhaps he is now in danger of proving that his world is going well, so what better time to expose its flaw and suffer a relapse? Misplaced perfectionism plays a part in this for he pushes himself to ludicrous limits to prove some worth, but is both chemically and emotionally unable to sustain the pressures.

As usual I emphasise that if these patterns are not recognised they only add to the well of despair. The self-hate will diversify into all aspects of the ex-alcoholic's life – from the subtleties of the marital bed to actual suicide.

I CANNOT FACE MY PAST

Remorse, like self-pity, is a futile and destructive emotion which tends to pervert the course of all other feelings to its own ends. The victim requires a metaphorical slap in the face to pull himself together. We have perhaps achieved the slap and now must complete the exercise by rebuilding the self-esteem.

Firstly, it should be clear to you by now that in no way were you responsible for your alcoholism. It is the result of a chemical change of which you had no knowledge. Your past was a predictable multiple symptom. It is also likely that you were genetically predisposed to acquiring the condition.

It would be foolish to ask you to dismiss the consequences of your illness without a thought, for you have to keep them in mind if you are to go forward, not backwards. But there is no place, and no reason for guilt. Instead you have a duty, a duty to be responsible for yourself in the future, to explain where necessary the nature of the illness you had, and to know it yourself, and to proceed with confidence and courage, not guilt.

AA asks you to make amends where possible, except where to do so would be injurious to your self or others. It may not be appropriate, for example, to tell Fred that you tried to seduce his wife during an alcohol induced moral dilemma. Do not indulge yourself, but just take practical steps to correct the inadvertent harm you have done. A sincere apology and explanation will go a long way. Do not jeopardise your own sobriety by yet again trying to achieve the impossible.

Having discarded the guilt we can proceed to the next stage, which is appreciating the real you. Once you value yourself again you will have no need for the defences that cut you off from the world. A time of honest integration and evolution lies ahead.

WHO AM I?

If you are to cope with life you need to understand the discrepancies between your view of yourself and the views of others, for it is over-emphasis on the latter that leads to the defences mentioned. One way to make an honest self-appraisal is to construct twenty answers to the question 'Who am I?'

The first few will be straightforward: name, sex, marital status, social class, job, interests and body image. These are essentially roles, as opposed to personality traits which follow, such as 'I am generally honest', 'I have little sexual morality' or 'I hate cruelty'. Remember, you are compiling this list for yourself only, so there is little point in deception. Include achievements and those matters in which you take pride, as well as failures and weaknesses.

Problems may arise from the lack of absolute values, so it may be preferable to use a five- or seven-point scale between two extremes. Any variety of characteristics may be included, but some possibilities are:

strong/weak	dominant/passive
aggressive/docile	selfish/unselfish
honest/dishonest	proud/ashamed
kind/cruel	responsible/irresponsible
patient/impatient	passionate/unfeeling
loyal/disloyal	sociable/anti-social
tolerant/intolerant	determined/weak-willed
heroic/cowardly	sexually moral/immoral

When you have finished you might ask yourself whether you are prepared to show this for confirmation to someone else, and if not, why not? If you *do* show it to others, you may be surprised by their additions or modifications, for we are often too modest. When you have struggled through this it will help you obtain a better assessment of how you feel about yourself.

Morality is largely convention, and it is reasonable to expect that not all conform in their beliefs. As regards self-esteem, it is most important that you do not contravene your own personal moral code, which may be at variance with those of others, providing, of course, that it is not just a morality of convenience. For example, many people who both preach and practice a very free sexual morality become much more circumspect when committing their actual beliefs to paper. This suggests that their actions are contrary to their actual beliefs.

We can learn a great deal about ourselves and our beliefs, as opposed to our behaviour, by undertaking an honest moral inventory. One way of tackling this is to re-examine some of the headings given above such as honesty, patience, tolerance, unselfishness, pride, responsibility and morality and look into them more deeply. For each one write a statement of belief, how you interpret it and why you feel it to be important. Having done this try to recall instances in which you acted according to your beliefs and others in which you failed. Note the consequences in each case. Names, dates and places are useful in 're-living' the experience.

The interesting point is that most people can think of many examples of acting contrary to their beliefs, but have great difficulty in recalling those occasions when they followed them! It seems we see no big deal in behaving honestly! This type of moral inventory allows us to reconsider and even challenge our beliefs, and highlights the extent or not to which we follow them. We begin to know ourselves.

By far the most effective, and perfectly valid way of increasing self-esteem is to ask as many people as you wish (the more the better) to write down what they consider to be your best qualities – those for which they most admire or respect you. It is probably best to restrict their choice to three qualities and by comparing a number of lists you can gauge which are the three qualities most often mentioned. Incidentally, the people do not have to like you, for overt fans may be hopelessly biased. It is surprising how unaware you may be of some of your good points.

STARTING ALL OVER AGAIN

You should by now have learnt some pretty nice things about yourself, and no doubt you can remedy some of the not-so-nice, since you have recognised them. So how about tidying yourself up generally, add a touch of colour, even give yourself a treat or two. *Feel* good.

I start each day just reminding myself that life *is* a precious gift and should be used well. Perhaps you could do something similar; it does help. Do not forget that by far your greatest ego-booster, and one specific to you or others recovering, is the fact that you have attained sobriety, albeit 'just for today'. And having indulged in all this introspective analysis, start looking out, for that is the best way both to stop dwelling on your faults and to remedy them.

Sobriety, honesty and real love. Little else is needed. Stop trying to please others. Be yourself. You do not have to smile all the time, nor need you constantly apologise. Just be you.

9 Learning to Live Again

THE MIRACLE THAT IS US

Nature must have concluded that although, for all practical purposes, instinct provided a very workable computer-like basis for living, it was somewhat restrictive, and not much fun. In her wisdom she therefore bestowed on us the magic ingredient of free will. She thus absolved herself from considerable responsibility and produced neurotic man.

Man frequently forgets just how fragile and vulnerable he is, and sees no great credit in merely surviving his allotted three score years and ten. Yet every second, billions of molecules in his body conspire to produce miracles of molecular architecture and maintain the status quo. The main aim of all this appears to be to allow a brain to absorb energy, to eliminate anything which is undesirable or unnecessary, to move around and recognise its surroundings and finally to produce replicas of itself to perform similar functions. We only understand a fraction of the elaborate messenger-system that relates every part of the body to the whole, and confers the essential unity we know as life. And although it would seem to ask sufficient of the brain that it coordinates all of these activities in a rational manner, acting as an overseer, it also has powers of thought and feelings far in excess of those needed for mundane survival. 'Who am I, what am I doing, where am I going?' dominate much of our thinking but are hardly necessary for survival.

This 'surplus to requirement' concept should not, I feel, be ignored. Man has an extraordinary ability to offer some near-mechanistic explanation for every facet of life. The logic of A going to B which must go to C, fails dismally when it is impossible to define A in the first place, or explain its origins or its purpose. The subtle yet immense difference between logic and real understanding is not always made clear. Thus, no matter how logical an evolutionary sequence we can postulate for the world, we can neither explain the original space that accommodated the original matter, nor conceive of any purpose in it. And whilst we may interpret the transformation of the sex drive into love and inspiration, or the stimulus-response system of the brain into creativity and philosophy, in terms of either sociobiology or gene survival, we fail to ask why such complexities are necessary. A far simpler model might suffice; after all nature is the supreme economist. We could say that our spiritual inclinations have helped our survival, yet I suspect there could have been far simpler and less fallible ways of achieving the same. I accept that our individual values, and the collective mores of society, contribute to the survival of the species, but I do not readily accept that they are only genetically determined biological necessities.

Purpose is essential. So do we assume that nature obliges by implanting the image of a mythical God, or the mental equipment to construct philosophies. How very elaborate. Why implant the need in the first place? The drives of sex or food are perfectly adequate for the ant or bee. It has been pointed out that Man is as yet a very incomplete evolutionary product, largely imperfect and excelling only in intelligence, the full potential of which has yet to be developed. (The spiritual evolution of Bergson and Ouspensky.) Yet this intelligence is also seen as the greatest threat to the ultimate evolutionary goal. A very chancy process indeed, and hardly endorsing a logical A-to-B survival system.

The minute we were given free will and choice we were taken off automatic and left on manual, with more responsibility and freedom. Of course it is a lot more fun that way. So much fun, in fact, that we cannot wait to play with our freedom, tumbling over each other in our efforts to experience everything and explore its potential. We push everything to its limits exactly as a child does with a new toy, and with much the same results. Is it surprising that we repeatedly damage ourselves?

Most of this damage results from conflict. We have only to recall our self-valuation scales from the preceding chapter to know this, placing ourselves between emotional extremes such as courage or cowardice, kindness or cruelty. We constantly ask ourselves questions we cannot answer, or seek goals we cannot achieve. We have to be responsible to others as well as ourselves, live up to expectations, respond to challenges, satisfy demands. We have to take risks. And whilst faced with these problems we are governed by a variety of forces that rarely work in perfect harmony: our instincts, conditioned reflexes, behaviour patterns, attitudes, biological drives, intellect, emotions and spiritual yearnings.

Life is unique in being self-regulating, self-servicing and self-motivating. We have mentioned already some of the networks of communication concerned. They not only dictate the harmonious symphony of being, but attend to our primeval needs. Yet all this forms no more than a repository for our experience and learning, the foundation for choice. A framework for decision making and problem solving, and the constant 'thoughtful' dialogue with ourselves and our environment that defines our individual beings. Our molecular dynamism has to balance with the environment to form a functional whole, and the forces involved defy speculation.

Stress is inevitable, and indeed necessary. Our reaction to stress is analagous to that of the immune system, requiring assault to build a defence. A normal stimulus-response system. Those who limit their stress, or who are protected from it will act adversely to the inevitable emergencies. For optimal development both our minds and bodies require constant and appropriate stimulation. Lack of stimulation will lead to atrophy, even death.

Our natural reaction to injury, whatever the reason for that injury, is to defend ourselves. The protective wall we build isolates us from the offending environment and limits the stimulation. Yet it is this stimulation that is essential to our recovery. The real danger is that our instinctive defences become incorporated into our behaviour patterns and are not recognised for what they are. They continue to operate long after the removal of the initial threat, and form a permanent obstruction to our living. Only by recognising these defences and somehow breaking them down can we hope to recover.

We have seen that we inherit differing amounts of essential equipment, and acquire more as we proceed through life. We respond to stimulation and usually benefit thereby. Efficient development is attained by finding the optimal environmental conditions, neither too much nor too little, whether we are talking about exercise, diet, sun, sex, acquisition of knowledge or stress. The challenge should stretch our abilities, and requires taking risks. Life can either polish or destroy the genetic inheritance. It sounds harsh, but not if we assume we play an active part.

Alcoholism presents a special case of damage, unique only in the specific use of alcohol as a defence. As I have said before, I am convinced that the familial factor in alcoholism can be accounted for by a genetically determined adverse reaction to stress. There is not so much an abnormality, as a personality that is less comfortable than that of his normal counterpart, and which discovers that alcohol removes this discomfort, and permits him to function normally. If he makes sufficient use of alcohol, then the ensuing chemical events will lead inevitably to the self-perpetuating mechanism we have seen. Without any knowledge of the damage he has done he cannot avoid the bizarre emotional disturbances that follow. These are essentially defences against his feelings of guilt and shattered self-esteem, also creating a further demand for alcohol. Not only will the emotional and behavioural defences prevent his adequate participation in life and communication with the environment, but the addictive process by its very nature will result in alienation as a progressive monomania. Whether an addiction results from lack of motivation elsewhere, or leads to a loss of outside interests, the ultimate effect must be the same. Non communication. The alcoholic has therefore to deal with three areas in his recovery. The initial problem, should it exist, the chemical damage and the resulting emotional defences.

As alcoholics we have withdrawn from life and cease to relate properly with our environment. It requires both acceptance and a conscious effort to re-enter the system, expose ourselves again with honesty, take risks and continue to evolve. We can only function normally again if we are prepared to, willing to take our rightful place in the whole dynamic equilibrium we know as life. No longer obliterating our conflicts, but acknowledging them and resolving them.

The real miracle of our lives is our adaptability, the ability to change according to circumstances, which lies within us all. The way in which we use this to overcome adversity defines the quality of our beings and transcends all material or mechanical concepts of life. We need to restore value and quality to our lives and have spiritual purpose. Faith does not require proof. Let us accept our intellectual limitations. Life has to be considerably mightier than the mightiest thoughts or utterances of those who borrow briefly from it. We only borrow a fraction yet dare to cast judgement on the whole.

THE WAY AHEAD

Most people are naturally anxious to know what sort of programme they should follow for a positive recovery. Most treatment centres include a variety of therapies aimed at improving the mind and body such as simple exercises, occupational therapy, yoga, meditation and spiritual guidance. They exercise the patient's discipline through a variety of domestic duties. In effect, they are attempting a form of whole body therapy designed to re-orientate the individual back to normal complete living, which is in agreement with the philosophy just expressed. This general approach will invariably outrage a few who deny needing the therapy. Considering the non-selective nature of addiction it is likely that individual needs will vary enormously. Perhaps the most important feature common to all therapies is that they represent social activities stimulating the mind or body, and carrying some sense of personal and group responsibility, together with the essential element of discipline. A revision crash-course in living.

I have no wish to insult the reader by telling him how he should occupy his days! The whole point of this book is to give the reader back his life, and allow him to accept responsibility for it, with the underlying principles of sobriety, discipline and purpose.

The need to avoid all mood-altering chemicals has been explained, and the effects of withdrawing from these described. It has been stressed that medical advice or help may be required initially, but that the doctor must be aware of the nature of your problem and your chemical dependence. You are also aware that total recovery will take some time, and during this time you will be particularly vulnerable. The emotional complications, negative defence systems and the effects on relationships are all described, and the need for honesty in rectifying these faults stressed. But it is not enough just to read these once, read them again and think about them, particularly as regards how they affect *your* life. Train yourself to recognise traps, defences, dangerous behaviour patterns. It is too easy to fall back into negative behaviour particularly in the early stages of recovery. It is impossible to overemphasise that no matter how enlightened or wary you believe yourself to be, guilt, battered self-esteem and resentment, in particular, will remain your biggest threats. Recognise them for what they are, and the danger they carry.

No matter how convinced you may be that you were not responsible for your problem, you may still feel very uncomfortable about it. What you are really experiencing is not guilt, but a deep sense of shame. We all have a sense of shame and it may be evoked by a variety of situations. Shame is encapsulated in the fable of the Garden of Eden: shame in our bodies, shame in our thoughts, shame in exposure of our shame. We can often exonerate ourselves from guilt but not shame. We can feel shame for others, shame for world starvation, shame for humanity exposing its weaknesses. It need not involve personal guilt. So recognise this feeling and know you share it with the rest of humanity. Welcome back! The danger lies in not recognising the cause of your discomfort and perverting the feeling into some other classical defence such as anger or resentment. With alcohol or drugs you were exposed, and you cannot avoid a sense of shame whenever you are reminded of it.

Of course you are resentful of the effect alcohol or drugs have had on your life, but hopefully you have learned how to express your

A-I

grief over the losses incurred. You will be reminded of your losses again. You will be reminded of your damaged self-esteem. And as you recover, there will be other losses which you realise for the first time. Be prepared to recognise the insidious resentments for what they are.

BUYING TIME

The more you distance yourself from the problem, the less arduous the journey, so it should go without saying that temptation is best avoided in the early stages. Again, there are no hard and fast rules, for only you know what poses a threat to your sobriety. I believe that recognition of a danger area is more important than avoiding it. Know when you might be at risk. More subtle and therefore dangerous pressures are exerted by 'euphoric recall' – the association of drinking with particular events or moods. Only you will recognise these and know which old habits or situations to avoid. In general, I believe most of us do know when sobriety is being threatened but sometimes choose to take the risk. Be careful that this is not a packaged excuse for having a drink.

An extension of these situations, and one that can be more hazardous in that it operates largely subconsciously, is that of the conditioned reflex. Pavlov demonstrated that not only would a dog automatically salivate on sensing food, a reflex action, but that it could learn to respond in the same manner to a 'dinner-gong' by association, a conditioned reflex. This is a very useful device for biological survival, allowing an immediate and unthinking response to a variety of stimuli. Unfortunately we may be unaware of the manner in which during our journey through life we have conditioned ourselves to respond to a variety of seemingly uninteresting stimuli. It seems reasonable that bells remind us of church, or Fred walking down the road of opening time; but we may be bemused if a scrap of lace throws us into frenzies of erotic desire, or a nostalgic song drives us back to the bottle. We have to be cautious of the traps we unwittingly set ourselves. They may play a significant role in promoting behaviour patterns, including those of drinking. Conditioned reflexes may account for the otherwise unaccountable urge for a drink.

I believe that an even bigger threat can be posed by fear of a drink, making a career out of abstaining. Commitment to sobriety, yes, but it should not dominate your life, for that only expresses your insecurity. The emphasis should shift from 'I cannot drink' to 'I do not wish to drink'. And when you have bought enough time, then the sooner you return to normal, full and confident living the better. But be wary of premature or misplaced confidence.

Should a relapse occur, all is not lost. I am not condoning the relapse, but should it happen your response has to be that of positive resumed recovery, not defeat. It is the last approach that can reinstate the whole chronic cycle of guilt, remorse and resentment. Take your own responsibility for it, and do not be affected by the judgement of others. And do not make that 'slip' an excuse for a binge.

If you wish to find guidance for many of the problems that will beset you, then Alcoholics Anonymous will provide not only this but regular stimulation, reminders of purpose, and answers to the very real problems peculiar to sobriety, as opposed to those incurred through drinking. This is not always fully appreciated. Long after the drink situation has passed certain problems will arise that cannot be appreciated by family or non-alcoholic friends. These can be shared with AA. It is also important to realise that AA teaches a way of life, not just sobriety; that this way of life confers sobriety is a bonus. Feelings, values, behaviour, relationships and spiritual implications are freely discussed. If you are foolish enough to think you know it all, then maybe it is time you helped others. But you will probably be surprised. Thousands have been helped to sobriety through AA and gone on to find serene and rewarding lives. They also provide both interest and friendship.

DISCIPLINE

In a way this involves little more than accepting responsibility for yourself and others in a reasonably ordered manner. Routine can be boring, but absence of it catastrophic. Whether you are a super-executive or unemployed, it is likely that the ravages of drink or drugs have eroded your attention to daily detail, whether it be brushing your teeth effectively or making that telephone call. Discipline should really apply to the mind behind the action, but is evidenced by the action. Be responsible again. You know.

BE GLAD YOU ARE AN ALCOHOLIC

We have stressed that although you must put the unhappy aspects of your drinking past behind you, you should not dismiss it. You also learned a great deal from this experience, knowledge which you can now use. There is another dimension to your alcoholism that you may not have considered. I believe that the very aberrations of the gene which predispose certain individuals to alcoholism in the first place might also confer some benefits. There has always been some association between addiction and creativity, particularly in the case of alcoholism. A variety of explanations have been proferred for this link, such as curiosity, a desire for widening of experience and awareness, or even the quest for some eternal truth! I think Koestler is right in suggesting that drugs cannot add to the creative content of the brain, but that they might facilitate its expression by removal of blockages or inhibitory processes. They might normalise certain individuals. I found that on occasion alcohol effected this, allowing greater clarity of expression, although the effect was somewhat limited to the first drink or so! I am sure many have experienced this. It is of greater interest to consider that creativity and alcoholism might have a common root cause, a genetic hypersensitivity to the environment. This might confer exciting attributes of curiosity and imagination, but these taken to extreme lack the practicality necessary for survival. Bergson claimed that our senses were limited to those permitting survival, and it may be that the alcoholic personality is maladjusted in sensing too clearly and too well for its ultimate good. Perhaps my overreaction to situations in early life led to my use of alcohol to avoid over-stimulation in later life.

The alcoholic personality is like a car with no brakes, fast but hazardous. Whether or not that individual makes use of alcohol as a somewhat erratic braking system is a separate issue. The alcoholic personality is not doomed to alcoholism (and neither is alcoholism the prerogative of the alcoholic personality). It is vitally important to stress, however, that whatever benefits these inherited personality traits may confer, the exercise of these qualities does not require alcohol or drugs, indeed the qualities will be destroyed by them. Used wisely, these gifts add to your self-esteem. If you feel, or experience, excessively then enjoy the beauty and care about the pain. Whilst we have been drinking we have been overwhelmed by the latter, to the exclusion of the former. Now we have been given the chance to remedy this. The world is littered with geniuses who never touch a drop for they use their talents too wisely. Too many alcoholics masquerade under the banner of frustrated genius.

DAMAGED PEOPLE

In a sense there is nothing unique about the alcoholic or the drug addict, they are only particular cases of damaged people who have used alcohol or drugs as a defence and escape. Most people suffer some damage during their lives and considering the huge demands made on such a sensitive system this is hardly surprising. Many people recognise the warning signs of unacceptable stress very quickly and adjust their lives accordingly, but others fail to do this and have the scars to show it. Deep within them lies the wounded self-esteem, and the visible scars are anger, resentment, envy, jealousy and false pride. There are many casualties that we tend to dismiss as recluses, dropouts, eccentrics or just that 'irritable old man or woman round the corner', withdrawn or defensive, and cut off from normal society. And somewhere between these and normality are thousands suffering intermediate damage.

Some find escape in work, sex, eating, do-gooding, religion or unconsciously in chronic ill-health. These escapes and many others – even hobbies can become a form of addiction – offer an alternative to real living. More dramatic temporary relief is found in a nervous breakdown, or permanently through suicide. So do not indulge in self-pity when you recollect your sick behaviour; it is shared to varying degrees with much of humanity. Your specific problem is that you sought escape through alcohol or drugs, only to find that these increased the damage, accomplishing in a year or two that which otherwise might have taken a life-time, or even not happened at all. And all these people without their defences and self-imposed hang-ups are in reality nice people who have lost their way.

Ironically, as we have seen, the cure lies in the very thing people run away from: life. Nature provides the challenge, the means of choice and the remedy should the choice be wrong. It involves no more than recognising oneself as a whole person again, and rejoicing in the knowledge.

We are surrounded by challenge, all we have to do is respond. There is beauty to be enjoyed and ugliness to be cared for. You have a body and mind demanding stimulation, not the previous anaethesia, so use them to relate to the world outside yourself. Go out and start living. Boredom is an indulgence of the selfish, for need is everywhere, and help takes many forms, from a simple smile, kindly word or helping hand, to active voluntary work in the community. It is your life, but it is to be shared. Take it out and enjoy it. Spiritual purpose represents a real need that requires satisfaction. It does not matter exactly what form your beliefs take, it is the searching that matters. The answer is anywhere and everwhere giving substance to the illusion we call reality, a child's smile, an erotic experience or a Beethoven symphony. Cling to your aspirations and your belief in yourself and in life. The ability to share in the excitement and beauty of life is your strength. It is something greater than yourself that provides the motivation for recovery and living. Once you have discovered this miracle there is no need to seek escape from it. The art of living is a journey, not a sudden revelation. Daily you will find increased awareness and inner strength, happiness and knowledge of real love. You had it, to some extent, but you lost it. It will be stronger than ever when you find it again, for it will be strengthened by experience and self-knowledge.

The whole of life is waiting for you to reach out for it. Use all aspects of your being, mind, body and spirit, and look after them.

A Personal Postscript

Compiling any work of non-fiction should by definition carry considerable responsibility, and I am particularly aware of this in the present volume, the whole subject being far too serious in its implications to allow of any misrepresentation, accidentally or by design. The printed word can assume compelling authority, so any conjecture or personal view should be made abundantly clear to the reader. It is for this reason that I have chosen to add some entirely personal comments separately in this final section.

I do not believe there is any such animal as the 'alcoholic'. Not in the sense that some individuals may suffer from a catastrophic metabolic flaw which renders them incapable of handling alcohol. I see the word as no more than a convenient term to specify someone who suffers from alcoholism, a condition to which no-one is immune, resulting solely from chronic alcohol abuse.

Every individual experiences stress, and the basic mechanism by which the body copes with stress is common to all, but the extent both of that stress and the response of a particular body to it may differ widely. Similarly, the physiological modus operandi of alcohol is the same in all individuals; but the degree of need for its anaesthetising effects will vary according to the sensitivity of the individual and the stress imposed. These are quantitative, not qualitative differences. Stress will vary according to circumstances, but underlying the whole is a strong genetic element that initially dictates our reaction to any given stress. It follows that the need for alcohol is determined both by the personality of the drinker and the circumstances to which they are exposed. A continuing sizeable need constitutes addiction and alcoholism. Even an individual without any initial personality 'hypersensitivity' may unwittingly potentiate alcoholism by continual exposure to undue stress and the attendant use of alcohol to moderate that stress.

In all individuals, prolonged and excessive use of alcohol will damage the natural response mechanisms of the body to stress, which, in turn, will create a greater need. I believe this to be evident to some extent in many 'steady' drinkers who feel they have no problem. When without alcohol they become clearly less comfortable in a variety of demanding circumstances which in previous times, when they drank little, or not at all, posed no threat. In a minor sense they have come to depend on alcohol. They are using a chemical to manipulate their brain chemistry and create an appropriate mood. Perhaps they have lost the ability to induce that mood naturally.

I state this, not as an indictment against drink in any shape or form, but to emphasise that alcoholism, as generally recognised, is largely a question of degree. The significance of the hackneyed phrase 'I need a drink!' depends entirely on the size or urgency of that need, and this is what separates the social drinker who uses alcohol to relax, from the very anti-social drinker suffering from alcoholism. There is no 'Us and Them' in this game, only people, although some will be far more susceptible to alcoholism by virtue of an inherent personality trait and/or, to a lesser extent, circumstances. The 'Us and Them' philosophy is a convenient promotion for those who benefit from the sale of drink, or politicians who see the merits of exports, considerable employment and inland revenue! It provides a sop to the moralists who do not wish, for a variety of reasons, to aportion any blame to alcohol per se, and provides a convenient excuse or defence for millions of drinkers who assume it cannot happen to them! But by far the greatest danger lies in the failure of society to recognise the embryonic or latent symptoms of alcoholism. Because we blind ourselves to the real nature of the condition, we fail to diagnose the problem until it becomes extremely difficult to deal with. With a startling lack of subtlety, we rely on such extreme symptoms as early morning or secret drinking, withdrawal symptoms, selective amnesia, even DTs or fits in order to diagnose the problem! And then we are surprised that the individual so diagnosed experiences difficulty in abandoning his or her addiction. We expect them to cast off years of chemical and emotional outrage and adopt a course of action which only too often we would find abhorrent ourselves.

I trust that in these pages I have made it abundantly clear that by this time the individual concerned is very, very sick, far more so than can be detected outwardly, or is recognised within. This has probably been true for some time, possibly years. In no way can they be held responsible for the lifestyle they have adopted, which is governed solely by a chemical demand amidst emotional chaos. Their only salvation lies in their understanding exactly how and why they are sick, and knowing that this is also appreciated fully by those around them. Condemnation or recriminations are not only out of place, but chronically counter-productive. It has to be recognised by all concerned that it is a rational disease requiring an equally rational treatment.

The reader may be forgiven for wondering where personal responsibility lies in this problem. Are we absolving the 'alcoholic' and blaming circumstances rather than individuals, as we all too frequently do for others who offend against society? I think not. Personal responsibility requires an understanding of both the nature of the choice and the consequences of that choice, neither of which is fully available to the potential 'alcoholic' in the very early, but crucial stages of the disease. Because we do not wish to know about the darker side of alcohol, we frequently hand over responsibility to the 'alcoholic' when it is too late. Indeed, we condone many of the less extravagent excesses. A whole attitude has to change.

Responsibility, I suggest, lies in education. Education regarding not only the true nature of alcoholism, the insistent need, but the whole *raison d'être* of alcohol. We would greatly benefit from a better education in the nature of stress, and the ways we can best cope with it or escape from it. Of great immediate importance is an understanding through education of the earliest sinister signs of dependence. We need to recognise the state at which our need for a drink first overrides rational contra-indications or simple will. This is the stage at which we have to acknowledge that alcohol has become too powerful in our lives, and attend to the problem before it becomes too deeply entrenched. At this stage it will have had, mercifully, little effect on the broader areas of our lives, and virtually none on the people around us, and would be, I believe, amenable to relatively painless intervention as a treatable condition. GPs should be trained to be more alert to the earliest signs of incipient alcoholism and the hazards of prescribing tranquilisers for the myriad of drink related 'stress' symptoms often presented, and be more prepared to confront the patient with the truth, a rational explanation and the real need to do something about the problem and why. Compassion does not include evasion. There is something incongruous in assuming that only by allowing a disease to develop sufficiently will the patient be motivated to do something about it, particularly when that stage may coincide with the point of no return!

In this book I have frequently expressed my admiration and respect for Alcoholics Anonymous, which I endorse again, but this might seem contradictory to some of the comments I am now making, particularly my dismissal of the term 'alcoholic'. Perhaps the simplest way to answer this charge is to state that there is much I do not accept in the teachings of the Church, but I believe in 'God', in Christ and his teachings, the power of prayer, and I go to church! And I know that I gain thereby. The practical evidence for the vital role of AA is overwhelming and nothing short of miraculous. In the final analysis, if an individual cannot cope with his alcohol problem he can find salvation with AA, who not only have a proven pathway to sobriety but can tell us much about leading a fuller life. We should not be blinded by detail when looking for truth.

A further question might occur to the reader. If a person suffering from alcoholism does not differ fundamentally in a biochemical sense from their normal counterpart, why is total abstinence recommended following recovery? The answer is that it is not possible to state exactly how long complete recovery takes, nor to define the precise extent of the damage. It is not possible, as yet, to exclude the possibility of irreversible damage, or a remaining hypersensitivity to alcohol which would continue to pose a threat. There is also the risk that an alcoholic personality will always be at high risk, whatever his or her understanding. And if, knowing this, we are still tempted to try again, are we not admitting to the very need that we accept as the danger sign? This has to be the point of individual responsibility, awareness of choice and acceptance of the consequences, and in this sense I deplore those academics who choose to offer impersonal advice without having experienced the void. There is no greater sobering thought than that stimulated by the statistical evidence. This book asks no more than that people recognise themselves and their circumstances, and take control of their own lives once more.

Acknowledgements

Alison Thomas whose interest, advice and friendship was invaluable in the preparation of this book.

Oxford University Press for kind permission to quote from *The Nightwatchers* by David Gascoyne. From *The Collected Poems of David Gascoyne*.

Bibliography

Badawy, A, A-B., *British Journal on Alcohol and Alcoholism* (1981) *16*.4. p.157

Dawkins, R., *The Selfish Gene* (Oxford University Press, 1978)

Glatt, M., *The Alcoholic and the Help he Needs* (Priory Press, 1969)

Goodwin, D., *Is Alcoholism Hereditary?* (Oxford University Press, 1976)

Greer, F. G., *The Journal of Alcoholism* (1972) 7.4. p.131

Hamilton, W. D., *The Genetic Evolution of Social Behaviour* (1964) R. J. Theoreti. Biol. 7 p.1.

Heather, N. and Robertson, I., *Problem Drinking: The New Approach* (Penguin, 1985)

Hughes, J., *British Journal of Addiction* (1976) *71*. p.199

Jaret, P., *National Geographic* (1986) *169*.6. p.702

Jellinek, E. M., *The Disease Concept of Alcoholism* (Hillhouse Press, 1960)

Kessel, N. and Walton, H., *Alcoholism* (Penguin, 1965)

Lovelock, J. E., *Gaia: A New Look at Life on Earth* (Oxford University Press, 1986)

Patterson, M., *Hooked? N.E.T. The New Approach to Drug Cure* (Faber and Faber, 1986)

Rodgers, J. E., *Science Digest* (1983) *91*.1. p.60

Wene Goedde, H. and Agarwal, Dharam P. (eds), *Genetics and Alcoholism. Progress in Clinical and Biological Research*, Vol 241 (Alan R. Liss, 1987)

Wilson, E., *Sociobiology: the New Synthesis* (Harvard, 1975)

Wilson, E., *On Human Nature* (Harvard, 1979)